# In the Field
## with
## Teilhard de Chardin

Bust of Teilhard de Chardin by Malvina Hoffman

# IN THE FIELD
# WITH
# TEILHARD DE CHARDIN

George B. Barbour

HERDER AND HERDER

1965
HERDER AND HERDER NEW YORK
232 Madison Avenue, New York 10016

Library of Congress Catalog Card Number: 65–13490
© 1965 by Herder and Herder, Incorporated
Printed in the United States of America

# CONTENTS

# FOREWORD

In the introduction to his book, *Teilhard de Chardin. Scientist and Seer*, the late Dr. Charles E. Raven acknowledges that it was a visit to Dr. George B. Barbour in Cincinnati which made his own interest in Teilhard first catch fire. Dr. Raven urged that an account of Teilhard's field-work be written down before the details were forgotten. The result was the present manuscript, which Dr. Raven saw and discussed in its early stages. Four days before his death, he wrote to Dr. Barbour:

"We don't want popularity and big sales for little books about Teilhard: we want to have the world shown that here was a man not like Barth—or me—sitting in a library and spinning fancies or even scholarship, but living a full, varied, and consistent life in surroundings of universal importance; and drawing from such a life of letters full of human interest and divine insight. Your Chinese adventures are of intense historical importance already, and will be far more when we get rid of atomic panics. To scale them down to the journalist's level of a week in Tibet is to increase the danger that Teilhard was a mere hammer-and-magnifying-glass collector of fossils, who had as a priest to color his life with pieties and speculations. . . .

"After a wide scrutiny of the contents of your manuscript, let me tell you how happy I am with it, and how for me it illuminates not only the scenes of his life, but his own quality and work. It is . . . eminently readable—much more than a record of him—it is a fine picture of China and elsewhere at a very critical period of history; the quotations of his letters keep it always human and contemporary."

Dr. Raven was originally to write the foreword to this book, but his death has left the task to me.

Soon after Teilhard and I met in Paris in 1946, I began to realize that for many years we both had been thinking along parallel lines, trying to consider man *sub specie evolutionis,* at one and the same time a product of past evolution and an active agent in its further course.

We both realized that, in the million-year passage from subhuman to human, man had stepped across a critical threshold, and left the slow-moving biological phase of evolution for the new, faster-moving, and increasingly mind-directed psychosocial phase, in which evolution is manifested by changes in ideas and societies and cultures rather than in organisms and their genetic constitution.

In this, we were both backed by long years of professional concern with evolution—myself as a general evolutionary biologist of the neo-Darwinian brand, but with excursions into religion and other psychosocial fields, Teilhard as geologist, paleontologist, and anthropologist, as well as a Christian priest and member of a religious order.

It was because he knew the facts of his science at first hand in the field, all over the world from Europe to China and Africa, that he was able—or rather, compelled—to attempt the task of applying them to his religious beliefs.

This linking of evolutionary biology with Christian theology, it seems to me, is his unique contribution to thought, enabling thousands of Christians to accept the greatest scientific discovery since Newton—Darwin's discovery of the evolutionary process as a fact and as a scientifically explicable phenomenon—and so pave the way for the eventual reconciliation of science and religion, which will come when the religiously minded understand that theology needs a scientific foundation, and grasp the fact that religion itself evolves, and when the scientifically minded accept the equally basic fact that religion is part of the evolutionary process, and an important element in its psychological phase, of human history.

I always regretted that Teilhard had neglected to explain and discuss the mechanisms of biological evolution as well as its results in its long temporal course, and I was quite unable to follow him in his conclusions about Christification, Point Omega, and the like. But this in no way detracts from his essential achievement of linking science and religion across the bridge of evolution.

Another of his great achievements was as a geologist; in the field, or at his desk, Teilhard was equally thorough and interested in the subject at hand. In these pages, Dr. Barbour has provided us with a picture of Teilhard as geologist in three continents. Besides being enjoyable reading, his book renders us the service of describing the rich background against which Teilhard worked. To those interested in Teilhard de Chardin, as geologist-paleontologist as well as philosopher, Dr. Barbour has offered generous insight.

SIR JULIAN HUXLEY

# In the Field
## with
## Teilhard de Chardin

# INTRODUCTION

FEW men in history have become so soon the subject of such a flood of interpretation and range of appraisal, by so diverse a group of self-appointed assessors, as has Pierre Teilhard de Chardin. Within a dozen years of his death, one may even read the verdicts of commentators on the critics of his interpreters.

The main stages in the development of Père Teilhard's thinking have been set forth in Claude Cuénot's biography[1] and in the same author's more condensed study recently issued in paperback.[2] Teilhard's earlier growth stands out in sharp relief from the pages of *Genèse d'une pensée*, a collection of his letters written in the trenches during the First World War. The cousin to whom he was writing at that time did the world a service by assembling the two series of *Lettres de voyage*. The English edition combines both in one volume, under the title *Letters from a Traveller*,[3] and is introduced by a vivid essay on "Teilhard the Man" from the pen of his long-time colleague, Pierre Leroy, S.J.

Probably the most discerning appraisal by a scientist of his own generation comes from a man who never met him. Charles Raven's *Teilhard de Chardin. Scientist and Seer*[4] gives the English reader a more convincing portrait of the man and his thought than anything else that has yet appeared. In his foreword to *The World of Teilhard*,[5] the late John LaFarge, S.J. brought out in a sensitive sketch some factors in the trying conditions under which Teilhard strove to fulfill his destiny of sharing with others his panoramic vision of life. LaFarge drew attention to Teilhard's

13

craving for understanding, his intense loyalty and his utter integrity, as well as the frustration under which he labored.

Read against this background, some letters which Teilhard wrote to me as a fellow geologist show the way in which he reacted to obstacles he met, and are characteristic of the man himself. These letters, for which I am responsible in English translation,[6] were written mainly in the decade covered by Chapter 8 in this volume. To place the letters in proper context, it is essential to sketch the setting in which Teilhard was working. A brief history of his life (Chapter 1) is therefore followed by an account of the men who were his co-workers in North China during the late twenties (Chapters 2–4), of experiences shared in Central and North China in 1934 (Chapters 5–7), and of our later contact in South Africa and the United States (Chapter 9). For these I have drawn freely on field notes made at the time, on geological reports printed after our return from the field, and on daily letters sent back as a running *compte rendu* to my family on the other side of the globe.

Large parts of my letters dealt with people, local situations and personal matters that had no connection with Teilhard. Passages quoted verbatim from my originals have been edited only where necessary for clarity, coherence or grammar, but without the usual symbols for lacunae, expansion of abbreviations, etc., with which most of the paragraphs would otherwise have been heavily marked. Throughout, the spelling of Chinese place-names follows the modified Wade romanization adopted by the Chinese Post Office, and used by the National Geological Survey to which Teilhard was attached, rather than the spellings found in Teilhard's letters and on French military maps.

I am grateful to M. Joseph Teilhard for permission to use the excellent portrait of his brother, which his family sent to friends at the time of Pierre's death. Likewise, it is a pleasure to express the honor felt when Sir Julian Huxley consented to write the Foreword.

14

I am under debt to Mrs. Davidson Black, Claude Cuénot, Ernest Gherzi, S.J., Jeanne Mortier, Malvina Hoffman, Charles and Ninette Raven, as well as to my wife and my sons, who with other friends of Père Teilhard have made helpful comments during the slow evolution of this book.

G.B.B.

*Cincinnati*
*January 1965*

# 1

# Biographical Sketch

PIERRE TEILHARD DE CHARDIN was born May 1, 1881 at Sarcenat in the Puys District of Auvergne in Central France. His mother was the great grandniece of François-Marie Arouet, known to the world of letters as Voltaire. Pierre was the fourth of eleven children, who grew up as a closely knit circle on a grassy estate west of Clermont-Ferrand before leaving their "eagles' nest" to follow careers around the globe—at sea, in the army, in business, mining and science, and in the service of the Church.

Pierre's formal education began in 1892 at the Jesuit college of Notre-Dame-de-Mongré near Villefranche-sur-Saône, thirty miles north of Lyons. He passed his first baccalaureate in 1896, and his second, in philosophy, the following year. In 1899 he entered the Society of Jesus, served his novitiate at Aix-en-Provence near Marseilles, and took his final vows at Laval in northwestern France. When the religious communities were secularized at the turn of the century, he migrated with other members of his Order, first to the island of Jersey in 1901, and then—in 1908, after a three-year interval spent as Instructor in Chemistry and Physics at the Jesuit College of St. Francis[7] in Cairo—to Ore Place near Hastings in Sussex where he completed his philosophical and theological studies.

Both on Jersey and at Hastings, an associate of his was Father Ernest Gherzi with whom he used to hunt fossils. Like the familiar White Cliffs of Dover, the chalk of the Sussex Downs near Hastings is studded with flint nodules and cretaceous shells. The bedrock rifts readily, and a slight tremor is often enough to dislodge an unstable block and send it crashing to the base of the cliff. One resounding blow on a flint concretion may detach a heavy rockfall. When Gherzi saw Teilhard making for a promising fossil outcrop, it was his role to step back to the water's edge and look up the face of the cliff, in order to shout a warning of any threat of sudden death from above. Twenty years later, when Gherzi was director of the Siccawei Observatory in Shanghai, it was he who suggested his friend's name to the head of the Chinese Geological Survey when the latter was looking for an expert advisor.

In 1911, Teilhard was ordained to the priesthood. The following year he came under the influence of Marcellin Boule at the Museum of Human Paleontology in Paris, and in 1913 he joined Abbé Henri Breuil on an expedition to the prehistoric sites in the Pyrenees. Boule had recovered a rich haul of early mammalian fossils from Quercy in the southwest of France, and turned them over to Teilhard for study. Further fossils from the Rheims area became the basis for his later dissertation on the mammals of the Lower Eocene Period, and set the trend for his subsequent interest in early primates, including the forerunners of man.

During the First World War, instead of seeking an army chaplaincy, Teilhard chose to serve as a stretcher bearer with the Second Regiment of North African Zouaves and Sharpshooters. He was cited several times for conspicuous bravery, and received the *croix de guerre* and the *medaille militaire,* but he consistently refused promotion beyond the rank of corporal. After the war he was decorated with the cross of the Legion of Honor. As already noted, the letters which he wrote from the front line have been published under the title *Genèse d'une pensée.*

On demobilization in 1919, Teilhard returned to Paris, studied for his graduate degree in natural sciences at the Sorbonne, and rejoined the team now working with Henri Breuil at the Museum of Human Paleontology. In 1922, he was appointed Associate Professor of Geology in the Catholic Institute in Paris. Despite his growing stature as a scientist, his ideas on transformism in relation to the evolution of the primates, and in particular an address on original sin delivered at the Institute, brought him under criticism from his ecclesiastical superiors. As a result, a consistent effort seems to have been made to play down the importance both of his biological and of his theological ideas. He was told to shun the more speculative aspects of his field, confine himself strictly to descriptive paleontology, and avoid any interpretive writing on the meaning of the facts he had discovered. He was forbidden to publish on the latter theme during his lifetime. Though his manuscript *Le phénomène humain*[7] was printed posthumously through the sponsorship of his friends, a notice sent to directors of seminaries after his death, and a *monitum* from the Holy Office in 1962, still warned Catholics against the danger of reading Teilhard's writings. It is likely that, as the result of the present Ecumenical Council, a change in this negative attitude will come about.

In 1923, Teilhard was sent to China to work with Père Emile Licent, S.J., who had established a museum of natural history in the Jesuit college at Tientsin. Together they made expeditions across the North China plain and along the borders of Mongolia. In 1929, Teilhard was appointed advisor to the National Geological Survey in Peking. This led to an invitation from the American Museum of Natural History to join Roy Chapman Andrews' Central Mongolian Expedition in 1930. While in Paris the following year, Teilhard was urged by Georges-Marie Haardt, director of Citroën's "Croisière Jaune" (Yellow Expedition), to be one of an auxiliary party going up from Peking to meet the main group when it entered Chinese Turkestan west of Kashgar, and to make the west-east traverse of Sinkiang and Outer Mongolia. The primary purpose of the two-year expedition was to prove the feasibility of using Citroën's half-track cater-pillar tractors for exploration over rough terrain. As a result, the party moved at the maximum speed possible with a heavy load of stores and camp equipment. This limited Teilhard's detailed geological observations to places where petty official interference, washouts, road blocks and other obstructions delayed progress, or when overnight halts were made near wells or Mongol settlements. An account of the difficulties surmounted by the expedition is chronicled in the official report.

In 1929, following the discovery of the teeth of Peking man (*Sinanthropus pekinensis*) that same year, Dr. Davidson Black organized the Cenozoic Laboratory as a joint research unit under the Chinese Geological Survey, supported by the Rockefeller Foundation. As advisor and collaborator, Teilhard worked in the Lockhart Hall laboratory in Peking and at the Chou-Kou-Tien cave site. Upon Black's untimely death in 1934, Teilhard acted briefly as Director, until Franz Weidenreich, Professor of Anatomy in the University of Frankfurt, came from Germany to complete Black's work. That summer, Teilhard joined me on an expedition up the Yangtze to the Red Basin of Szechwan, and then across the Tsinling Range from the Yellow River into the Han Basin. He spent the winter of 1935–1936 first in India with the Yale-Cambridge party under Helmut de Terra, explorer and physiographer, in the Siwaliks, and then with the Harvard-Carnegie Expedition in Burma. During this same period, he found time also to do some field work in Somaliland and Ethiopia, besides paying two visits to Pithecanthropus sites in Java with G.H.R. von Koenigswald, Dutch anthropologist from Leyden.

After the Japanese Army overran North China in 1940, Teilhard's movements were sharply restricted. With Pierre Leroy, S.J., he organized the Geobiological Institute in the Legation Quarter in Peking, gathering there what could be salvaged of the material from the Tientsin Museum and the Cenozoic Laboratory. Here Teilhard continued to study and write scientific papers, essays and pamphlets, including most of those which he later revised for publication in book form. He began to set down his ideas on the evolution of man, projecting into the future the processes observed in the past, and forecasting, as Piveteau put it, "*la paléontologie de l'avenir.*" Returning to Paris in 1946 after the war, Teilhard found that essays, intended for private distribution, had been copied in unauthorized form, and widely circulated. They had appeared at a critical moment when the intellectual youth of France, disillusioned by the aftermath of war, faced a wave of materialism and uncertainty which bred pessimism and despair. Existentialism was inadequate for many thoughtful scientists. To such men, Teilhard's writings offered new hope.

In 1947, he was preparing to leave with me to join the University of California's Expedition to South Africa, when he suffered a heart attack. Four years later he had recovered sufficiently to carry through the plan on a much reduced scale, thanks to the support of the Wenner-Gren Foundation for Anthropological Research. Paul Fejos, the Director of the Foundation, had welcomed him as a Research Assistant and given him office facilities at its New York headquarters, to which he returned for the last years of his life.

Teilhard died in New York City on Easter Sunday, 1955.

# 2

# Tientsin

SUCH emphasis has rightly been placed on Teilhard, the philosopher and mystic, that it is hard for those who never met him to realize what he was as a scientist and a man. His was a very human personality, with an immense gift for friendship, and some very human faults and foibles; a man of great personal charm, strong loyalties, true humility and rare tolerance, able to accept reverses without loss of serenity, always hopeful, and a marvelous companion in the field.

It is not possible to form a true estimate of Teilhard's contribution to knowledge without some understanding of the Chinese setting in which he worked, and of the men with whom he associated.

Tientsin, where Teilhard first took up residence on arriving in China, was a "treaty-port," with the advantages and disadvantages of that status. Under the treaty of Tientsin in 1858, China had granted extra-territorial rights to nationals of other countries living in "concession" districts of all "treaty-port" cities. Two years later, by the Peking Convention of 1860, major powers which recognized imperial China by sending ministers to the capital were allowed to build "legations" in the southwest quarter of the walled "Tartar City" which itself surrounds the inner "Imperial City" with the "Forbidden City" at its core. Eleven such legations were standing in 1923, while the ministers of smaller countries rented quarters in hotels or other buildings nearby.

Each was a center of interest and social contact, not to say gossip, for the community of its nationals living in an alien land. When Teilhard arrived in Tientsin, these anachronisms still persisted. But by the time he left China, the rising tide of nationalism had swept them away.

The year 1923 was an exciting one in China. The young republic was barely a dozen years old. The Literary Renaissance was just getting under way, and a healthy ferment was at work. Many young Chinese, recently returned from overseas, had brought back from America, Great Britain, France, Germany, and other European countries a heady brew of new ideas—about science, self-realization, and the social order—that did not fit the classical pattern of life in old China.

Though passages in Teilhard's early letters make passing reference to these portentous stirrings, he did not fully awaken to their significance until 1929 when he moved his base to Peking, where this radical "New Thought Movement" had its roots. Teilhard's first assignment had been to Father Emile Licent's Museum on Racecourse Road in the French Concession in Tientsin. Living there under extra-territorial rights, it was easy for him to adopt the attitude of the visitor from outside, whose eye is caught by the quaint differences in the customs and reactions of the oriental.

Teilhard, like every newcomer to China, was given a Chinese name. In the traditional way, the surname comes first, like a genus name, and should properly be one of the "Hundred Family" (clan) names. The given name, like a species name, follows beneath, and usually combines two monosyllabic words which have some inner poetic or ethical meaning of special significance to the grandfather or scholarly friend who names the child. When naming foreigners, an effort is made to find some three-word combination which vaguely suggests to Chinese ears the sound of the person's name as pronounced in his own tongue. I do not know who named Father Teilhard—possibly some sinologue in his own Order—but his name was unusual and distinctive. Finding no surname closer than "Tien," the donor of the name took the word for "virtue" (pronounced *der,* but written *Teh* in the Wade romanization). His "given name" was

romanized as *Jih-chin;* the first syllable was spoken a little like the French *je,* and the second like *jin*—together faintly recalling the sounds involved in *Ch*[ard]*in* and meaning "day enter." This could perhaps be better rendered as "dawn" or "daybreak," with an overtone implying "progress from day to day," in the sense of Coué. Unconventional though Teilhard's name was, to the Chinese it stood for the man, and was more prophetic than his unknown donor guessed—"Father Daybreak Virtue." Teilhard could write the middle word (day, sun), but admitted having trouble with the first and third characters.

Just why Teilhard never made any serious attempt to learn the language of the country, I do not know. Possibly, after dispensing with the Greek and Hebrew needed for his *license-ès-lettres* and theological training, a knowledge of French, Latin, and English seemed a heavy enough load for any man to carry. Whereas those of us who were attending Language School looked forward to making China our home for long enough to justify the time and

23

effort it takes to struggle with the language, Teilhard had no such feeling of permanence. I used to tell him that the Latin motto carved over the hearth in my father's study in Edinburgh was more appropriate to him than to myself—*Ut migraturus habita:* "Live as if about to set out on a journey."

In any case, like many other great men, Teilhard was intensely proud of his own country and language, and saw everything through French eyes. Not being a born linguist, he simply was not interested in other tongues, useful though he knew they might be at times. Fortunately, the few educated Chinese with whom he was in daily contact spoke French or English. It is a tribute to Teilhard's sympathy and human understanding that the language barrier did not seem to lessen his influence. One reason for this was the winning smile in his grey-blue eyes, which needed no spoken word to be understood.

Imposing titles mean much in China. Emile Licent's *Musée Hoangho-Paiho* (named after the Yellow and the White Rivers, the greatest, and probably the smallest, watercourses on the map of the North China Plain) had just been established in a wing of the impressively named Ecole des Hautes Etudes, which was in fact a Catholic junior college for business students opened at Tientsin in 1923 by the Jesuits of Champagne. There Licent's natural-history exhibits attracted considerable attention. From time to time, he went up country, making circuits across the Yellow River Plain and into the hills of the northern provinces, recording and collecting as he went. Letters to the outlying mission stations preceded him asking that the Fathers report the finding of any "dragon-bones"—as fossils are called—or other items of interest so that these could be designated as museum property until Licent himself came to collect them.

To a Chinese farmer of the old school, any geologist is anathema, because he goes about striking rocks with a hammer—an act that cannot but disturb the spirits of the mountains and bring bad luck. For, as these farmers believed, *Feng-shui*—"the spirits of the winds and waters"—exert a fateful influence on the life of man and beast, and on the crops upon which both depend. At the same time, "dragon-bones" were regarded as specific remedies for a variety of complaints—and were, no doubt, as good for migraine and colic as aspirin or bread-pills. It was only reasonable to assume that the Fathers at the museum were doing rather a profitable business in dragon-bones on the side. More than one up-country villager asked me tactfully whether he should approach the stout priest or the thin priest for a prescription to cure grandfather's lumbago or little brother's sore eyes. While one may smile at this naïve faith in the Chinese pharmacopeia, it should be remembered that the same medical lore had found use for *ma-huang,* the root of a Mongolian shrub which yields ephedrin, and for the gland above the eyes of a toad, which secretes a white substance with the stimulant properties of digitalis.

The Belgian Fathers of the Vicariate of Jehol in Southeast Mongolia had printed a useful road map of their immense parish. Licent was determined to do something similar for Chihli (later Hopei Province), and prepared several large map sheets, along with descriptions of the highways. These were based on diaries in which he had noted each event of the route just as it happened. The journeys were charted in the simplest manner. Normally, Licent travelled with a "Peking cart" accompanied by a servant and driver. The solid axle of a Peking cart squeals as it turns, unless daubed at intervals with castor oil from a long-stemmed pot slung from the rear of one of the shafts. But every jolt of the heavy wheel is faithfully transmitted to the entire contents of the cart, including the back bones of all passengers. As anyone who has used this agonizing means of transportation knows, the wise voyager can easily keep up with this "prairie sampan" on foot, and with less physical distress.

Measuring the radius of the wheel, Licent made a chalk mark on one broad spoke, and calculated the distance traversed by counting the turns of the wheel beside which he was walking. At intervals, he would disturb the cook's slumbers, climb on board himself, and look at his watch. The beast could be relied on to make ten *li* per hour on the level. A *li*, the Chinese unit of distance, has a pleasing Oriental flexibility adjusted to the terrain. Measuring roughly at a third of a mile or, say, half a kilometre, the *li* tends to contract going up hill, and stretches on the downgrade, being in effect a function of lapsed time and energy expended. It is, so to speak, a unit of effort. For it seems farther from a village in the valley to the fort on the top of the hill, than vice versa. When a cluster of houses in the depression ahead promised a cup of tea at a stand by the roadside for the driver, and a drink of water for his beast, both could attain a speed of a dozen *li* per hour. Everyone understood and all were satisfied. Licent simply made allowance for such fluctuations in his calculations.

Directions were plotted from compass readings taken at every bend of the road, checked by back-bearings to the previous turn. Each was carefully recorded in a notebook, for transfer to a base map on return to Tientsin. For longer trips, provision had to be made for bringing home the fossils and other specimens destined for the museum. Licent was an excellent organizer and a formidable collector, a man of stout physique with a commanding presence, who knew what he wanted and would leave no stone unturned to get it.

Within a month of Teilhard's first arrival in Tientsin on May 22, 1923, he and Licent set out on their first long trek to the Ordos bend of the Yellow River, as he tells in the first chapter of *Letters from a Traveller*. Those chapters have the vividness of first impressions, and combine Teilhard's keenness of vision, his appreciation of the wide expanses of the Mongolian Plateau, and his sense of the beauty in nature—all depicted with a poet's feeling for richly flavored words.

In those days, the narrow-gauge railway from Peking up the Nankou Pass to Kalgan, extended only as far as the railhead at Paotou on the left bank of the Yellow River. There Licent organized a sizeable party comprising ten mules, three donkeys, five muleteers, two servants, and the scientists, with a military escort. The original intention was to cross to the right bank at once and go directly to Ninghsia on the other side of the great Ordos Loop. But word of unsettled conditions in the desert region led them to revise this plan, and they made the entire circuit on the northern bank, along the exact line of the ancient caravan route that is followed today by the westward extension of the railway line. As a result, they passed the famous section at Sjara-osso-gol where the previous year, on the advice of Fathers Mostaert and de Wilde of the Belgian Mission, Licent had gone to a place where they had found fossils and Old Stone Age tools. From there, Licent himself had retrieved a rich haul of Quaternary vertebrates and a single human femur. And here, beneath a 30-foot blanket of buff colored windblown dust ("loess" to the geologist), Teilhard and he now found three more Paleolithic sites and related fossiliferous layers. By the time they reached Ninghsia, the caravan had grown to thirty animals, loaded with over three tons of specimens packed into six dozen cases. The muleteers were then paid, and the two scientists, with their hoard, drifted on a barge down river to Paotou, their starting-point. The entire trip beyond the railhead had taken four months and covered more than six hundred miles.

Early the following summer (1924), Licent and Teilhard made a twelve-week circuit around Jehol, the most southeasterly province of the Mongolian Plateau where all the streams drain into Manchuria. This trip gave Teilhard his first ideas of the broad structural framework of North China, ideas which he gradually developed into a major concept of continental geology. This was also his first opportunity to see the young volcanoes that reminded him of the Auvergne skyline of his boyhood. In addition to these major expeditions, Teilhard also made a two-day field trip with Licent across the Yellow River Plain to the south. Otherwise, the rest of that first year went to preparing and identifying their "*butin*" (loot), as Teilhard called it.

In June 1923, Dr. Charles P. Berkey, geologist on the First

Central Asiatic Expedition of the American Museum of Natural History in New York, asked me to try to resolve the discrepancy between the expedition's findings and the accepted age of certain formations exposed inside the frontier of China Proper, that is, immediately south of the outer line of the Great Wall. I therefore spent the latter part of the summer of 1923 trying to clarify the discrepancy.

I had met Teilhard at the winter meeting of the Chinese Geological Society when Licent and he reported on their Ordos finds, and had spent part of a day with him in the northern sector of Tientsin discussing questions relating to some large *Lamprotula* (freshwater shells) brought up from the bottom of a well there. But it was only during my second field season at Kalgan in the summer of 1924 that we had a chance to work together on a new problem. In the previous August, one of the original difficulties had been settled by the discovery of some plant fossils which were then sent to London for identification. A letter written to my wife on August 22, 1924, has words that foreshadow a constructive partnership which was to last till Teilhard's death.

Four miles west of Wan-chuan

It is very peaceful here under the stars, with Mars closer than it has been for a century.

The last few days have added singularly little to what seemed clear last year—amusingly so! At several points P.T. made some pretty radical suggestions that are at variance with my own ideas, but against which I can advance no definite facts to the contrary. But in each case, he has gradually veered to my own point of view without further argument from me—rather giving the conclusions as his own impressions as to what *must* be the explanation, though equally at a loss to get final definite evidence in either direction! It is an abnormally puzzling area. Usually, after you build up a theory, new facts either fall into line and prove it, or else oppose it and rule it out. Here new facts are annoyingly inconclusive. My earlier impressions of last year seem still as likely as

28

ever to be correct. Even the fossils sent to Seward at the British Museum are better than anything we could find today after an hour spent hunting at the same spot, to within five feet.

Accompanied by Li Lien-chieh, one of my students, with a cook and a muleteer, Teilhard and I left the railway at Kalgan (Chang-Chia-Kou—the "Chang-family Gap") where a gateway through the Outer Branch of the Great Wall guards the pass and

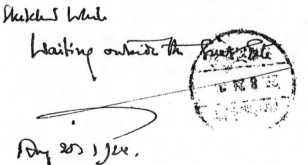

caravan route to the Mongolian Plateau. (A hasty sketch on a card, postmarked August 25, was penned while waiting at the ford as we returned, and shows the eastward continuation of the crude, outer wall up the rugged spur of Mount Williams.) From here, we struck due west to Wanchuan, the next walled settlement, which nestles under the abrupt step onto the upland plain. In Late Ice Age days, the same winds that swept coarse sediment into sand dunes on the pavement floor of the Gobi Desert, wafted the finer dust off the plateau lip to settle as loess, which makes the fertile soil in the valleys of the northern provinces. There it has remained as a national asset, unless washed away in the form of the yellow-grey mud that colors the Yellow River and the Yellow Sea. In early spring, dust clouds darken the sky till the midday sun is green. A single night's dustfall during one of the three-day "yellow storms" that afflict Peking every February dropped sixteen tons of dust on the city. Such adverse conditions readily explained the disappearance of the Early Stone Age man whose tools Teilhard and Licent had found under thirty feet of loess dust on their first Ordos trip.

Teilhard sailed from Shanghai on September 13, 1924, and did not come back to Tientsin until June 10, 1926. Within three weeks of his return he and Licent set out on an abortive attempt to follow the southern branch of the caravan highway system which becomes the "Great Silk Road" through Central Asia beyond Lanchow in Kansu. But civil war was in progress in Shensi and they were turned back at the Wei River ferry a dozen miles west of Sian. So instead, they crossed the Yellow River into Shansi and worked north through the loess highlands. Getting back to Tientsin at the end of August, they then spent three weeks in the Sangkanho Valley, collecting fossils from a lake deposit which I had visited at Teilhard's urging in 1924 when he had to leave for France. At a meeting of the Geological Society, I had named this the Nihowan Formation, noting that it implied an important change in the regime of river erosion. It remained for Teilhard and Licent to bring back in 1926 a copious haul of fossils that were characteristic enough to be dated as very late Pliocene or basal Pleistocene—distinctly older than the faunal assemblage being found at Chou-Kou-Tien, and hence of importance in setting a date to Peking man.

In June 1927, Teilhard made a second journey through Jehol, lasting ten weeks and almost reaching Dalai-Nor. In August, he returned to Paris, coming back in March 1929, to find that much had happened during his absence. Peking was now Peiping. Licent had more fossils to label. Even before his last departure for Paris, Teilhard was restive and disillusioned with the mercantile atmosphere at Tientsin. He had also come to realize that Licent was at heart a collector, more interested in naming and labelling the stone tools and fossils they found than in working out their wider meaning as keys to past history. Unlike Teilhard, Licent was more concerned with seeking the "what" rather than the "why," "when," and "how" of the new found evidence of ancient life which the specimens indicated. To record the trivia of daily incidents along the route seemed to Teilhard a waste of energy unless they led to an organized effort at drawing scientific conclusions of wider import from the outcrops of exposed bedrock, and at determining the age and sequence of formations. Moreover, Licent had become obsessively jealous of the prestige of his Museum, and was not a little envious of the standing accorded to Teilhard by the scientific group at the capital.

When the director of the National Geological Survey, Dr. Wong Wen-hao, had asked a fellow seismologist, Father Ernest Gherzi, S.J., for the name of a qualified geologist who might be invited to serve as Advisor to the Survey, Gherzi had no hesitation in suggesting Teilhard, with whom—as we have noted—he had worked in the Channel Islands and England. When the invitation came, Licent virtually closed the Museum doors to Teilhard. Their last trip together, in May 1929, took them into

31

Manchuria and on almost to the Siberian border at Julun-Nor. Teilhard then went back to Tientsin to prepare for his move to Peking. Strangely enough, although Teilhard had spoken of Gherzi as a friend, it was only thirty years later that I learned of the hand Gherzi had had in his appointment to the Cenozoic Laboratory. It seems probable that Teilhard himself was never aware of it.

# 3

# Peking

EARLY in June 1929, Teilhard set out for the loess highlands of Shansi and Shensi, on the first trip he undertook as a member of the Chinese Geological Survey. He was back in Peking by September 20. On October 17, we both went down with Dr. Davidson Black and Dr. Wong Wen-hao to inspect the progress made at Chou-Kou-Tien. Later, in November, Teilhard and H.S. Wang went with me up the Liu-ho Valley into the Chaitang Basin of the Western Hills.

When going into the field, Teilhard exchanged his clerical garb for a khaki drill suit of military cut with four large tunic pockets. A folding penknife, hand lens, marching compass, and loose money went into his trouser pockets. The padlock key of his kit-box was on a loop of string in his watch pocket. Bank notes and his passport went in an inside breast pocket, because the left upper pocket always carried his breviary, while the right one held matches and a crushed packet of Job or Gauloise cigarettes. The right side pocket held his small shiny black notebook with graph paper. The contents of the left pocket were apt to vary with the occasion—a folded map, a piece of string, a chip of lava, a fossil wrapped in newspaper, or even an unfinished square of chocolate wrapped in silver paper.

Whereas I used colored crayons in my field notes to distinguish formations, Teilhard always insisted that his stylo or pencil stub—often blunt and much licked—was enough. Other observations, he claimed, should be stored in one's head. He carried a lightweight mineralogist's hammer with a short head, and always had a chisel handy for detaching fossils. He never carried a rucksack or water bottle, and he used an army-type haversack only when out fossil-hunting or if lunching in the open.

When Teilhard joined the Andrews expedition, he was issued a loose sheepskin jacket, with a turn-up collar for use on the wind-swept Mongolian Plateau in cold weather, instead of the black cape he preferred at lower altitudes. With the jacket went a fur lined cap with large ear flaps of the kind worn by camel drivers. For headgear elsewhere, he kept a much used grey-black felt hat, replaced in hot weather by a blue beret or brown pith helmet.

On major expeditions, Teilhard always took an oblong black kit-box of sheet metal—three feet long and a foot deep—evidently a holdover from the First World War. Into this kit-box went whatever did not go in his pockets or into his bedding roll. Maps and papers lay on the bottom, beneath changes of field clothing, socks, underwear, a black wool sweater, and usually a thin cassock (for use whenever an overnight lodging at a mission outpost was likely to lead to a request that he say mass before setting out the next morning). Elsewhere, while the animals were being loaded, or when on a road that offered no special geological problem, he would take out his breviary, read the office of the day, and then sit in silence.

Into the box went also one or more metal cylinders to carry silver dollars for use in districts where the constantly changing issues of paper notes were suspect and less negotiable than silver pieces—though even the latter might be bitten by a canny merchant, or dashed down on a wooden counter to test its ring before acceptance. These silver coins—or Mexican dollars, as they were called before the Yuan dollars were minted—were stuffed into these tin containers with wads of crumpled newspaper to prevent the clink of the coins from attracting the wrong kind of atten-

34

tion. At this time, solid copper pennies, or *t'ung-tzu-erh,* were already replacing the old brass "cash" with a square hole in the middle. Cash could be threaded on a string and hung around the neck; but at three hundred to the dollar, they were as much nuisance as the devaluated small paper notes—originally worth a tenth of a dollar and eventually worth closer to one thirtieth— which were torn, dirty, and handled until their denomination was undecipherable.

In the open, Teilhard's spare figure seemed distinctly above average height—he measured just over 180 cm.—and he was fifty before his later characteristic stoop developed. He walked with the alert step of his army days, though with a slightly uneven gait; one foot—I think it was the right one—turned out a little more than the other. His vision was keen and far sighted. He began to wear steel rimmed spectacles only late in life, and then mainly for reading. Nothing of geological significance seemed to miss his eye. Once when riding a Mongolian pony across a gravel-strewn terrace in Jehol, he spotted a reworked Stone Age implement, where others had seen nothing but a patch of pebbles. Thirty years later when we were together in South Africa, he picked out two paleolithic hand axes on a former bank of the Vaal River from a spot which local archeologists reported as having been "picked dry."

Teilhard's field notes were brief, to the point, and illustrated at most by rough line sketches. These aimed less at reproducing what he saw than at interpreting in a generalized way the probable relation between the different rock units whose structure was often only partly exposed. Examples of these sketches appear in some of his letters, such as the last one he sent me from South Africa (see page 144). On the other hand, the outline drawings he made in the laboratory to accompany his published descriptions of a rodent's tooth or the jaw of an antelope were quite exact, and better than a photograph in emphasizing the diagnostic features of the species.

He used to regret his inability to sketch relief diagrams of the land forms we saw. He worked with a minimum of equipment, and dispensed with field glasses, aneroid, camera, and instruments of all kinds. When he was setting out for Mongolia, I gave him a small silver cigarette lighter, to reduce his high consumption of matches at the expense of a few drops of fluid from any fuel tank on the expedition. On his return, he apologized for having left it in the Gobi Desert, "somewhere near latitude 45° north and longitude 105° east of Paris," reminding me thereby that I had overlooked the fact that evaporation in Mongolia was so rapid that he had to draw on the expedition's fuel supply every second morning. Wisely, he relieved himself of its extra weight.

When out working together in North China, we were on the road at an early hour, so as to assure quarters for the night well before dusk, unless we planned to stay at a mission station or in the rest house of a railway company or mining concern where we were expected. Sometimes we put up at an inn—either in an open courtyard, under the stars with the animals, or else on a corner of the k'ang (adobe platform), which served as bed for all comers—at other times in the outbuilding of a temple, or on the elevated platform of a village theatre. The latter had the special advantage of satisfying the curious, while keeping them from coming too close. For our appearance was sure to be widely gossiped about in the town for the next month. Glass panes being unknown in country villages, the window frames of a caravan-serai are stretched over with white paper, like Japanese soji. Paper is translucent and shows shadows, but is not transparent enough to allow any audience participation in what were re-garded as the funny doings of the queer "foreign devils." How-ever, a well-licked finger can be worked round and round, until a small hole is made which affords a closer view. After dark behind each such peephole, an eye would reflect the light of our candle and let us know that our silent audience was missing nothing.

36

Expenses were kept down by living off the land as far as possible. When we arrived for the night, and had found a spot for our folding camp cots, the cook would start a fire, and then forage for noodles, eggs, an occasional chicken, "turnips which tasted like pears." Our wooden supply box—which came home loaded with rocks and fossils—furnished the extras: sugar, coffee, condensed milk, confiture, marmalade, tinned fruit, chocolate, candles, matches, and insect lotion. By the time we had washed up and changed shirts, water was boiling for a cup of tea. Teilhard would then hunt for his brown felt pantoufles with the red stripes, light a cigarette, and relax.

During the day, Teilhard's mind concentrated on the geological problems in hand. After supper, he would light another cigarette, and I would take out my pipe. Then, completing our field notes for the day, we would compare conclusions while they were fresh in our minds, and lay plans for the morrow. If a younger Chinese colleague was with us, he or the cook would inquire about conditions on the next stage of the journey. Spreading an oilcloth or a sheet of newspaper on the ground between our beds, we would undress, climb into bed, and blow out the light. Fortunately, in the north mosquito nets were usually unnecessary.

With the work of the day behind him, Teilhard would talk in the dark of the ideas nearest to his heart. I have often wished that I could have taken notes of things he said. Many of them were to reappear in more developed form in the later essays published after his death. But in those early days, he did not know of Drummond's *Greatest Thing in the World* and *Ascent of Man,* or of the Gifford Lectures. Although some of what he said did not seem revolutionary to me, a Scots Presbyterian, my own training was inadequate to follow his profounder thought, especially when he sought to look into the future.

He was clearly trying to draw together into a new perspective ideas from a wide range of sources which might give him a fresh outlook on the problems of science and religion. It was also evident that many of these ideas were innovations in Catholic thought, and that he felt he was treading on terra incognita. He realized that he was restating for the next generation an interpretation of human life and existence, an interpretation which he knew might have to be revised progressively as men became aware of new truth, regardless of its original source.

Conversation tended to become a kind of Socratic dialogue. As I recall, one night it ran somewhat as follows:

"George, did you notice in the last village those pitiful old men in rags, all with small branches of *saule* (willow) in their hands this afternoon? What were they doing?"

"Oh, probably it was the usual prayer for rain, when they carry the little image around the fields in a sedan chair to let 'him' see the awful condition of drought; meanwhile the suppliants hold branches above the image and over their heads as they pray to it to save their stunted crops."

"What could anyone say that would bring *any* comfort to these poor people? They live below the starvation level already. When it isn't drought, it is a flood. And they all live so crowded together. The world is getting too full, and, with people living shoulder to shoulder, we *must* find a new way to settle our differences without coming to blows to get what we need."

"Yes, it always seems to come back to material things in the end—money, stone axes or whatnot, with which to 'buy' what our bodies feel they cannot do without."

"But don't you think that if we were less selfish, we might feel the other man's needs also, and live peaceably with him in love, and perhaps rise to a higher level of spiritual life as a result? I am coming to feel that this is *the* key to the problems of the nations of the world. The Communists see only the material needs of people, and push forward to improve the living conditions of the masses. But they do not see the importance of the individual's need for upward spiritual growth. And perhaps the men of the

38

Church do not always feel the hunger and physical pain which these farmers must endure just to stay alive. Surely the path of future development must be the resultant of progress in two directions—forward and upward—at the same time."

"Or it might be a spiral, like a road up a mountain in the mist."

"Well, I agree, provided you continue to seek the summit."

Another night, Teilhard began by asking what I understood by the word "reality." I had to admit that defining it was hard. Solid objects are real in the sense that you can see and touch them. Yet emotions such as fear, hatred, and love can be stronger motives for action than a push from the rear by a water buffalo. Even a vivid dream or nightmare has a "reality" that may stir a man to do what reason alone would not bring him to try.

Teilhard insisted that such workings of the mind are just as truly parts of experience, and hence just as "real," even though on a different spiritual level, as facts that can be proved in a laboratory. He went on to observe that today few except doctors recognize that these are as truly part of experience and history as is material environment. In this higher category of experience in life lie the hopes and fears, the convictions of faith, and the other motivating desires and urges which make for human progress. These cannot be dismissed as "unreal delusions" that have no existence—though certainly delusions also exist. Even our senses may mislead us, as when one hand is placed in hot water, and the other in cold, before plunging both in a bowl of tepid water, which then feels both hot and cold at the same time.

One night in Honan, in 1934, Teilhard referred to the recent tendency to explain religion as an outmoded, primitive human weakness or superstition—which modern scientific discovery might make unnecessary—rather than as the true direction of spiritual evolution in the future, and the answer to the perennial question of the goal of life.

I remarked that we might as well blame our fishy ancestors

for the fact that each of us has grown a single flexible backbone, rather than a pair of shock-absorbing side bones to hold up our heads. Teilhard then launched on an analysis of the various religions which developed one after the other throughout history; he sought to discern what contribution each might have made towards a better understanding of the structure of the universe and towards a deeper comprehension of God. Religion is not just man's lazy reaction to his apparently insoluble problems, but is also the way to use his psychological energy in order ultimately to live on a higher spiritual level.

Talk was apt to start in English, with French terms—some of his own coining—interjected. As his thought went deeper, it slipped increasingly into his own tongue, until some question got an unintelligible answer, and he knew he had left me behind. By then, his cigarette was in ashes and my pipe had gone out. Finally, one or the other would say "*Bonne nuit! Dors bien!*" "*A demain.*"

# 4

# Peiping

PERHAPS the all-important period of Teilhard's life in Peking will be better understood in terms of his environment, and of the personalities involved, by a digression at this point.

Chinese cities have a pride that is shared by their citizens, and like them "lose face" when that pride is wounded. Thus, after the suppression of the Boxer Uprising of 1900, Tientsin was "degraded" by having its city wall levelled and replaced by a broad boulevard. This, it was felt, left the city unprotected, with its thoughts open to the winds and the evil spirits; however, a few years later it hastened a commercial expansion and prosperity from which the port city ultimately profited greatly.

During Teilhard's second absence in Paris, the government had been moved down to Nanking (the "Southern Capital"). This shift of power and reduced status were subtly emphasized by the change of name, which demoted Peking (the "Northern Capital") to Peping or Peiping (the "northern city on the plain").[8] But even though no longer the capital, the imperial city remained the intellectual heart of the country. For a decade it continued to attract the leading scientists, writers, and thinkers of the world. As many nationalities were represented in the polyglot scientific group to be found there in the late twenties and early thirties as at any time in the city's long history. The Academia Sinica, the Peking Union Medical College, the Chinese Geological Survey, and the various educational and missionary institutions acted as magnets to attract a steady stream of outstanding specialists from other lands. Away from their homes, such men were glad to lecture or chat informally, and we heard much that we would never have learned otherwise. Our guests of the early twenties included Bertrand Russell, Rabindranath Tagore, John Dewey, Sven Hedin, and dozens of others.

By 1929, Teilhard already had a host of friends in Catholic and missionary circles in Peking, as well as in the French and English speaking segments of the international community. His work for the Survey, especially in connection with the Cenozoic Laboratory responsible for the work on Peking man, brought him into close contact with half a dozen individuals whose views must have had considerable influence on his own thinking. The Chinese names he mentioned most frequently were those of Dr. V.K. Ting, Dr. Wong Wen-hao, Dr. C.C. Young, Mr. Pei Wen-chung, Prof. J.S. Lee and Mr. Eddie M.N. Bien. Two others of special importance were Dr. Davidson Black of Toronto, and Dr. Amadeus W. Grabau of New York.

Each of these eight men played a distinctive part in Teilhard's development as a scientist. Each touched his life in a different way. Their personalities were in sharp contrast. Each was making his own independent contribution to the intellectual renaissance which was paving the way for the wave of nationalism that was to sweep across the country. Half of their number are no longer living and the China they knew no longer exists. They are here given more than bare identification because they formed the group with which Teilhard was united by a common interest in the discovery of Peking man.

At the close of the First World War, Dr. J. Gunar Andersson, a Swedish prospector who had risen to become head of his country's Geological Survey, went out to China as Advisor for Mining to the Peking Government. Andersson was a giant of a man who once, when bitten by a rabid dog, heated a poker to red heat and plunged it into the wound, thereby cauterizing it effectively. His primary task was to suggest ways in which to develop the mineral resources of the country on modern lines.

In 1918, Andersson was examining a small coal field near Chi Ku Shan, in the Western Hills forty miles from Peking, when he came on a rich cache of fossils filling a red-earth pocket in limestone bedrock of Ordovician Age. He was impressed by the "modern" character of the fossilized animals, and resolved to come back with an expert. Two years later, he brought W.D. Matthew of the American Museum in New York, and Otto Zdansky from Uppsala, to confirm his opinion. They noted an even richer pocket in a quarry overlooking the village of Chou-Kou-Tien (the Inn at Chou's Gap). From a mass of fallen debris under the cliff, Andersson picked up several chips of white vein-quartz—a mineral not normally found in limestone caves. This led him to say prophetically, "Ah, here is primitive man. Now all we have to do is to find him!" As the result of two summers' digging, Zdansky collected a huge haul of fossils and shipped them back to Uppsala for study. Along with remains of dozens of other animal types, he discovered two teeth which at once became the subject of controversy. The teeth looked distinctly human. This find was announced by Andersson on October 22, 1926, to celebrate the visit of the Crown Prince of Sweden to Peking.

In view of the world-wide interest in Andersson's disclosure, Dr. Davidson Black, Professor of Anatomy and Neurology in the Peking Union Medical College, was able to enlist the support of the Rockefeller Foundation in his scheme for a Cenozoic Research Laboratory, as a joint enterprise of the P.U.M.C. and the Geological Survey of China. As early as 1922, Black had written to the Director of the China Foundation of the Rockefeller Board as follows:

All available evidence points to the conclusion that the dispersal area of mankind and his forerunners is to be sought somewhere in Central Asia. . . . the P.U.M.C. is in the singularly favorable position to promote

43

the study of racial anatomy, and thus become the foremost Eastern pioneer in the realm of investigations calculated to throw light on man's origin.

For two years, excavation at "C.K.T."—as the Chou-Kou-Tien site was abbreviated—was entrusted to Dr. Birger Bohlin from the Uppsala laboratories. He made an inch by inch study of the 80-foot height of exposed hill face. He found that there was no detectable change in the fossil fauna from top to bottom, implying that the entire filling of the fissure dated from the same geological epoch and therefore, though ancient, did not span any great length of time.

Three days before the close of his first field season, Bohlin exposed an excellently preserved left lower molar. Black unhesitatingly declared that the tooth's original owner had been human. He followed Grabau's suggestion that the creature be named "*Sinanthropus pekinensis*"—a model term, in that it is meaningful, clear, and without prejudice to whatever might later prove to be its relationship to the particular faunal genus into which we were born. Furthermore, it did not specify whether the creature walked on its hind legs, or lay on its back—merely that it came from Peking, and, being from the Land of Sinim, presumably talked Chinese, if it could speak. After all, the species was based upon the finding of a single tooth!

The following year, 1928, Bohlin was assisted by Dr. C.C. Young, who had just joined the Survey after working in the Munich laboratories of Professor Max Schlosser, an authority on vertebrate fossils, and by Mr. Pei Wen-chung, a brilliant undergraduate at the National University, where he had studied with Professor Grabau. Teilhard returned from Paris in March 1929, and the Cenozoic Research Laboratory was launched the following month with the following staff: Dr. Davidson Black, Honorary Director; Dr. C.C. Young, Assistant Director and Paleontologist; Père Teilhard de Chardin, Advisor and Collaborator; Mr. W.C. Pei, in charge of field work at Chou-Kou-Tien; and Mr. M.N. Bien, Assistant. The relation of the laboratory to the personalities on the Survey is unfortunately an aspect of Teilhard's life that has received too little attention.

In one of the early *Letters* (January 27, 1924), Teilhard wrote of his good fortune in meeting Dr. V.K. Ting-Ting Wen-chiang (or Ting Ven-kiang in his own province, and hence "V.K." to his foreign friends). Ting returned to China in 1912, after studying in the University of Glasgow, by way of Yunnan where he made his first significant contribution to science. As Professor in Peking National University, he gathered around him a group of keen young men whom he inspired with some of his own enthusiasm. The Geological Survey itself was his creation. Dr. Wong Wen-hao, his close friend and successor as Director, was not overstating when he spoke of Ting as "the founder of scientific geology in China." A brilliant linguist, astute diplomat, and sound administrator, Ting was an ideal choice as the first Director of the newly organized National Geological Survey. This was established on the advice of Gunar Andersson in his capacity as Mining Advisor to the government.

The language reform group to which Ting belonged was led by Dr. Hu Shih, the "Father of the Literary Renaissance," who had taken his doctorate in Philosophy in Cornell University. He had been appointed head of the Department of Philosophy at Peking University (Pei-ta) while Ting was head of the Geology Department. Hu later became President of the University, before going to Washington as Chinese Ambassador soon after the outbreak of the Second World War. (He continued to work quietly in New York until recalled to Formosa to be head of the Academia Sinica at Taipei.) While geology brought Teilhard and Ting together in Peking, Teilhard had not met Hu Shih until I introduced them in New York, where they had been living for some months within a short distance of each other on Park Avenue.

Ting resigned from the Survey in 1923 to devote his energies to developing the Peipiao coal field. The only possible successor as director of the Survey was his closest friend, Dr. Wong Wenhao, an able expert in seismology and minerology, who had been trained at Louvain and who spoke excellent French. In some ways, Teilhard felt himself closer to Wong than to any other man on the Survey. They had arrived from Europe at about the same time. But Wong leaned heavily on Ting's judgment long after the latter had no official connection with the Survey. Teilhard's own letters suggest that he discussed his advisory responsibilities to the Cenozoic primarily with Ting, even though the latter had not been with the Survey since Teilhard reached China. Wong was an astute politician, and when he left the Survey in 1935 quickly rose to Cabinet rank. This was six years after the government ministries and most of the departments had been transferred to Nanking. Fortunately for Teilhard, Wong managed to keep the Geological Survey in Peking.

Yang Chung-chien (Dr. C.C. Young) had joined the Survey in 1928, and being a northerner from Shensi Province, was closer to Teilhard's height than either Ting or Wong. We all appreciated Young's considerateness in not romanizing his name in the customary way, since Westerners confused the normal spelling, "Yang," with "Wang" (the "Smith" of China). Young shared Teilhard's enthusiasm for fossil mammals, and they worked together in the Cenozoic Research Laboratory which was housed in Lockart Hall, the science wing of the old London Missionary Society medical school building.

Two other Chinese geologists deserve mention. One was Bien Mei-nien, who had grown up in Hawaii and studied geology in Yenching University; and the last was Dr. J.S. Lee (Li Ssu-kuang), a graduate of Manchester, England, who after serving as head of the Geological Institute of the Academia Sinica in Nanking, was called to Peking National University to head the Geology Department early in 1934. His book on the geology of China is the standard work in its field.

The most remarkable figure of the group was Dr. Davidson Black, whose position and unique mental gifts made possible the Cenozoic Laboratory of the Geological Survey, and with it the opportunity that meant so much to Teilhard. Black secured his doctor's degree in the University of Toronto in 1906, but felt that the medical courses he had attended left serious gaps in his training. So the next winter he earned an M.A. in anthropology while acting as Assistant in Histology; he then went on to Western Reserve University in Cleveland, as Instructor in Anatomy under Wingate Todd. Following this, he crossed to Holland to study advanced neurology with Adrian Kappers, and finally worked with Grafton Elliot Smith in his laboratory in the University of Manchester. For good measure, he spent his evenings mastering the technique of plaster cast-making. Recrossing the Atlantic, Black visited the American Museum of Natural History in New York, where he won the friendship of the Director, Henry Fairfield Osborn, and Dr. W.D. Matthews, a fellow Canadian whose influence Black acknowledges in his monograph, "Asia and the Dispersal of the Primates."

After distinguished service with the Royal Army Medical Corps, Black joined the P.U.M.C. in 1920, and a year later became head of its Department of Anatomy. As has been stated, the finding of *Sinanthropus* led him to create the Cenozoic Laboratory. It was Black who saw the part that Teilhard might play on the team he was organizing.

Passing mention has been made of Professor Amadeus W. Grabau, the last of the group of Survey personalities with whom Teilhard was in constant contact. He came out from Columbia University in 1920. I accompanied Grabau on the last two field trips he made, but by the time Teilhard arrived in Peking, severe varicosity had already crippled him. Grabau was the inspiration behind the Geological Society of China, the monograph series of the Paleontologica Sinica, and the Peking Society of Natural History.

When Teilhard moved to Peking in 1929, he found quarters

with the Lazarist Fathers in the North Center of the Tartar City, spent his days mostly at the Cenozoic Laboratory in Lockhart Hall, and on his weekly visits to the Survey headquarters in the West City lunched regularly at Grabau's house on Fang Sheng Hutung nearby. Since the original financial provision, which was adequate when Grabau reached China, would not meet all his needs ten years later, Teilhard's generosity came to Grabau's rescue on more than one occasion.

In addition to the permanent members of the staff, in connection with special problems, Black enlisted the cooperation of any other available specialist who could be pried loose from his regular occupation. As a result, I found myself with the title of Visiting Physiographer to the Rockefeller Foundation and charged with the task of linking the recognizable stages in the development of the North China landscape with the conditions under which the cave deposit came into existence.

It was in this manner that what had begun as a casual contact with Teilhard became a direct personal relationship that was to continue for twenty-five years.

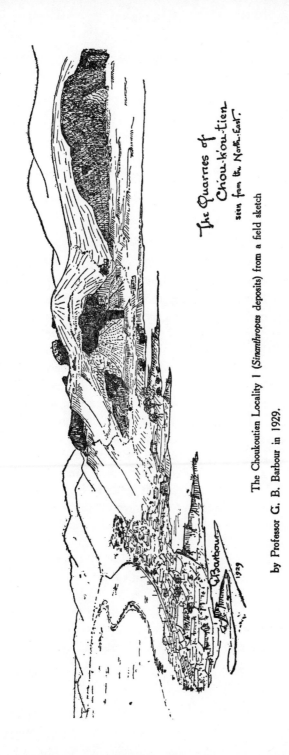

The Quarries of Chou-kou-tien seen from the North-East.

The Choukoutien Locality 1 (*Sinanthropus* deposits) from a field sketch

by Professor G. B. Barbour in 1929.

# 5

# Chou-Kou-Tien

WINTER came early in 1929. On October 17, Dr. Black and Dr. Wong Wen-hao took a party of us down to have a last look at the C.K.T. excavations before work closed down for the winter. The constant pall of blue-grey haze from the lime kilns made good photographs of the general setting of the cave hard to get. My assignment was to make a panoramic sketch for Black's report to the Rockefeller Foundation on the season's work. Six of us left Peking at 7:15 A.M., and there was ice on puddles at a few points along the road to C.K.T. The pit in which Pei was working had a northern exposure; since the sun never reached the bottom of the excavation, the ground had not thawed and digging had become much harder. Dr. Wong had already warned Pei by letter that it was useless to continue after the end of the month, and that we were coming down to inspect the progress made before everything was shut down for the winter. But when Dr. Wong joined us in mid-afternoon, he yielded to Pei's entreaties and told him he "might work for another week or two." Page 18 of my field notebook has a sketch of the south face of the cutting as it stood that day, with the fossil horizons exactly spotted—for by now *Sinanthropus* teeth and bone fragments had been retrieved from four different levels on the 80-foot vertical face of the excavation.

However, nothing new showed up during November. So at noon on December 2, Pei paid the workers at his room in the village, and climbed up the hill for the last time to measure the

18

(Wong after 3pm)
Pei
Teilhard
Black
Young
S.B.B.
also J.S.Wong

Chou·kou·tien· c'td .      17 Oct. 1929
Simplified sketch

Sinanthropus Locality 1.  4.30p.m. (looking 98°-105°)

Formations .... ① to ⑩ (in descending age)
Sinanthropus horizons. SA to SE (in order of discovery)

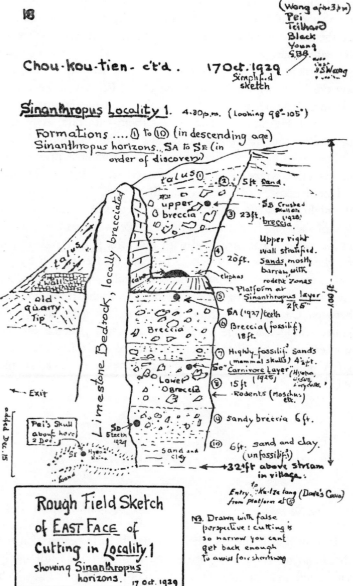

talus ①
② 5ft. sand.
upper breccia
③ 23ft. breccia
SB Crushed skulls etc (1928)

④ 20ft.
elephas
Upper right wall stratified. Sands mostly barren, with rodent zones

talus

Platform at "Sinanthropus layer" 2ft 6"
⑤
SA (1927) teeth

old quarry tip

⑥ Breccia (fossilif.) 18ft.
Breccia

⑦ Highly fossilif. Sands (mammal skulls) 4½ft.
50" "Carnivore Layer" (1928) (Hyena, Ursus, & cyclop.)
⑧ 15ft.
Rodents (Moschus etc.)

Lower breccia

Exit

⑨ sandy breccia 6ft.

Limestone Bedrock, locally brecciated

added Dec. 15

Pei's Skull about here 2 Dec.
SD 5 teeth 1929
⑩ 6ft. sand and clay (unfossilif.)

sand and clay
SE Hyena knive found
→ 32ft above stream in village.

to Entry. "Ku-Tze tang (Dove's Cave) from platform at ⑤

N.B. Drawn with false perspective : cutting is so narrow you can't get back enough to avoid fore-shortening

Rough Field Sketch
of EAST FACE of
Cutting in Locality 1
showing Sinanthropus
horizons.  17 Oct. 1929

exact dimensions of the hole. From these he could report the number of cubic metres taken out since work began at the end of the summer monsoon season. Probing with a yard-stick in the sand under a limestone overhang, he suddenly exposed the smooth dome of a skull, embedded in cave travertine.[9] Loosening the block with a hammer and chisel, Pei saw at once that the top of the cranium was larger than that of any ape so far unearthed. He carried it back to his room with care. A battery of candles from the village store had given just enough light for a time exposure of the find *in situ*. He got another photograph of his prize wrapped in burlap soaked with flour paste, and balanced above three braziers so that it could dry out during the night. By dawn, it was ready for the trip to Peking, without fear of shedding fragments on the road. Pei wrapped the treasure in his soiled linen, bargained with a ricksha puller, and set out for the city, the precious bundle between his feet hidden by the long skirt of his *ta kua 'erh* (Chinese scholar's gown). A minor civil war was in progress that month, and the front line lay between C.K.T. and Peking. But Pei rightly guessed that no sentry would challenge a college student going home for the weekend with his dirty linen. Pei covered the thirty-five miles safely and delivered his trophy to Davidson Black at the P.U.M.C. well before dusk.

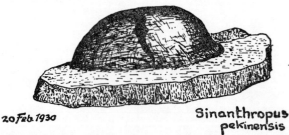

20 Feb. 1930
Sinanthropus
pekinensis

It seemed as if Black's whole life had been in preparation for that moment. The finding of the first well-preserved skull amply vindicated his fight for the recognition of the new genus of which he was to be the champion.

The separation of the soft bony braincase from its hard carbonate matrix, and the reconstitution into its original shape were carried out with meticulous care. Black did the delicate work in his laboratory alone and late at night when, as he used to claim, his hand was steadiest and his "night-hawk brain" worked most clearly. The corridors of the building were deserted. The door was locked against friends and intruders alike. Working with dental instruments, Black detached the encrusting matrix, grain by grain, before reassembling the individual head bones. At intervals, the skull was set up on a frame in the six cardinal positions, and he photographed it through a telephoto lens from the other side of the laboratory to reduce distortion due to foreshortening. The skull went back to its safe each night about 3:00 A.M. The films were developed the next day, and Olga Hempel, the Department Secretary, transcribed Black's notes. Prints from the negatives went, by different mails for safety, to each of three scientists scattered around the world in widely separated localities. For purpose of record, plaster replicas were cast, and three duplicates were made and painted exactly like the original by a skilled pottery artist working under Black's direct supervision. Each duplicate was compared with the original before being distributed like the prints. One of each type went to the British Museum, where it was copied by Frank Barlow, at that time the most skillful expert in his line in the world.

As a sample of the extreme care with which Black did everything relating to the work, the following rubric was pencilled in the margin of a scientific report that Black wrote a month after the skull came into his hands:

Final copy to XYZ with three carbon copies Jan. 29
D.B.
Original draft pages 1–3 Jan 9–12 (6 A.M.)
                pages 3–5 Jan 12–13 (finished 3:30 A.M.)
                pages 8–11 Jan 15 (5:30 A.M.)
First draft to XYZ Jan 16
Second draft to XYZ Jan 22
Final Jan 29                             D.B.

One is left wondering just when he wrote pages 6 and 7. It must have been before 4:15 A.M. on the night of January 14–15!

Such was the man who saw the significance of what Teilhard might do as a member of the Cenozoic team. As far as the hominid material was concerned, Black needed no help—after all, it was his own field of specialization. But he greatly valued Teilhard's independent corroboration of his own conclusions, and the discussions to which they gave rise. These latter, however, were concerned chiefly with the possible anatomical relationships between *Sinanthropus* and other extinct and living hominids, or with the stage of culture represented by the stone implements when these came to light later. They left unanswered the question of stratigraphic age, i.e., the precise geological epoch when the caves were inhabited by the primitive creatures—this would have to be decided on the basis of other criteria.

Methods of absolute dating—by Carbon-14, or the Argon-Potassium ratio—were still unknown, although it was the same Wenner-Gren Foundation that later opened its doors to Teilhard, which also underwrote Willard Libby's fundamental research on Carbon-14.

The stone tools found in the lowest parts of the C.K.T. diggings would only confirm the human character of the occupants. This was already suspected from the ashes on the floor, from the charred bones, cracked nuts, and broken bits of ostrich egg. But study of the associated mammal fossils—Teilhard's particular forté—did promise a time index of the relative antiquity. It could give the percentage of vertebrates which had evolved to modern type, as compared with the number of genera or species now extinct. In all, by then, over sixty distinct animal types had been found in the breccia and gravel layers filling the cavern. Many of the creatures were members of orders which Young had studied in Germany. Others were related to forms Teilhard had found in deposits of like age in Europe, Egypt, and elsewhere.

Teilhard was disturbed later to find that, as the man who

54

brought the Chou-Kou-Tien discoveries to the attention of the
French-speaking scientific world, he was often wrongly credited
with the actual finding of *Sinanthropus* remains. He was at pains
to disclaim this distinction, which was properly Pei's, Bohlin's,
and Black's. In this, Teilhard's feeling regarding the giving of
credit was in complete agreement with Davidson Black, who
wrote to me in October 1930:

> Just a line to tell you that I have just read with much interest and
> pleasure the abstract of your British Association note on the status
> of *Sinanthropus*. It has been prepared in the proper spirit of restraint,
> and with full proper acknowledgement of the Survey's work that will
> further the interests of our research. It is a treat to read a nice plain
> statement of facts in good English. Cheerio!
>
> D.B.

It was a stroke of luck that the famous cave, and the fissure
system to which it belonged, lay on the edge of a village community that had coal mining and limestone quarrying as its chief
sources of employment. This reduced costs and casualties by
affording an unlimited pool of native talent which could be
counted on to drill blast holes and light fuses without injuring
any of the workers.

By the time Teilhard arrived on the scene, the techniques of
excavation had been standardized. From an upper platform near
the cave, an overhead cable and pulley system, with counterpoised baskets, brought up an empty basket, gravity carrying a
loaded one down to the sorting platform 60 feet below. There
sorters labelled and wrapped the larger material, and hand-picked
everything else on sieves. Even stray teeth were caught. A small
field laboratory had been built, with space for storing specimens,
tools, etc.

Upon delivery at the P.U.M.C., hominid fossils went straight
to Black's anatomy department, while all other material was
taken to Lockhart Hall, where Teilhard and Young examined

it. After study, fossils were stored for permanent safe-keeping in the museum at the Survey headquarters in the West City, two miles from the Cenozoic Laboratory.

In May 1930, Teilhard went with Young and a small Survey party to the Great Khingan Mountains in Northwest Manchuria, returning in time to meet Roy Chapman Andrews and the other members of the American Museum's "Central Asiatic Expedition" which was then starting into the Gobi Desert. In view of tension aroused by the wave of Chinese nationalism, it was a wise move to invite the Survey to send representatives. Teilhard, Young, and later, Pei, were coöpted for the trip, which ended just in time for Teilhard to leave again for France in September 1930.

At Teilhard's urging, Henri Breuil came from Paris to China, but reached Peking in November 1931, while Teilhard was still in Mongolia. In the latter's absence, I was asked to escort the guest to Chou-Kou-Tien. Ten miles short of our destination, our car developed a puncture when crossing a bridge over one of the few streams on the road. While the tire was being patched, Breuil climbed down the bank, picked up a small boulder of chert, and within three minutes handed me a perfect Old Stone Age axe of Acheulian type. Again, in the laboratory at Chou-Kou-Tien, where the excavators had thrown into one pile all stones clearly foreign to a limestone cave found in the fossil-bearing zones, Breuil immediately picked out a half dozen which showed marks due to blows on the end. They must have been used as hammer stones by Paleolithic man.

In December 1931, one month before Teilhard got back to Peking, I had to leave for America on grounds of family health. It was late in April before I wrote to Teilhard from California, outlining my conclusions regarding the geology of the northwest region, which he had always hoped to visit. His reply was a typical geologist's letter, which would call for an explanation longer than the communication itself to be intelligible to the general reader. It merits inclusion here, however, as an example of the way in which his mind reasoned towards scientific conclusions drawing on detailed observations made over a wide region. The letter indicates the kind of evidence needed when trying to set extremes of antiquity to the epoch during which early man and his animal "associates" were living in North China. These lower and upper limits form a "time bracket" which was related to the prevailing climate, environment, and land relief. The letter was written from the Geological Survey offices, and enclosed a sketch map.

Peiping, 17 June, 1932

My dear George,

Your long letter of 30 April reached me safely, and pleased me greatly, because it gave me news of you, and was of special interest from the point of view of our joint research. I much regret not yet having been able to reach Lanchow. But what I managed to see last January of the Chungwei gorges south of Ninghsia makes me think you are certainly right about the presence, and the thickness of reddish loams in Kansu. South of Chungwei, approaching from Lanchow, you come upon reddish Sanmenian formations as soon as you get into the Huangho depression—there is not a trace of them farther west—only the famous "crust," of which I have more to say below.

There (south of Chungwei) the Sanmenian earths rest on a 50-metre terrace and are very rich in concretions, but extremely sandy. I am forced to interpret them as ancient sand dunes—showing a striking coincidence with the distribution of modern dunes. In any case, further up river (i.e., at Lanchow) one ought to find an equivalent formation. The *Lamprotulas*[10] do not seem to have got so far.

What you say about the localization of the "Fenho Stage" corresponds exactly with my own observations. As you suggest, that stage seems tied up with an upwarp of the Shansi platform (see sketch map). This uplift seems to have been going on since the Pontian conglomerates, which I know of *only* around Shansi.

On this very point, I must tell you that on a walk north of Mentoukou, I recently found in large quarries in Ordovician limestone, the same two types of pockets that can be seen at Chou-Kou-Tien, with rounded pebbles (connected with an alluvial fan or terrace) 100 metres above the level of the Sangkanho today: and cutting these ancient fissures, a network of cracks filled with fossil-bearing travertine. I am increasingly suspicious that the gravel pockets are Pontian in age. Whereas the fossil pockets extend right through Grabau's Polycene ("*I hate this term*"). Last year in the mountains west of Chentefu, I thought I also detected that there is a diminishing series of fans, a continuum of conglomerates running from the Pontian to the Lower Pleistocene. That would be the normal regime between Shansi and the coastal plain. Further north, in Jehol, everything is nested, rather than being deployed,[11] and the distinction between the phases becomes harder.

1 = poche ō graviers
   (alluviales)
2 = poche ō fossiles
   (sub-aériennes)

I send you herewith a sketch map on which I have indicated a series of facts that I should like you to consider.

(1) Note first the extreme localization of the *unquestioned* Pontian formations. There are enormous masses of Red Earths of possibly Pontian age in Jehol, Shantung, and between the Alashan and Tarim, but no one has found a single index-fossil. It is extremely annoying.

(2) Then note the wide distribution of what I call the "Sanmenian crust"—a carapace and conglomerate of sandstone, 5 to 10 metres thick, completely capping the old terraces and fans in arid regions. As I think I already told you, this gravel lies with abrupt contact on fine clays which are gravel-free.

There must be a tectonic—as well as a climatic—reason for the development of these Sanmen gravels on the high plateau. And the climate is equally responsible for the formation of the "crust." Was there at one time *above* the gravels a distinct bed of fine-grain material, since swept away by wind? I think so. In any case, I do not go along with Young's (highly confused) ideas about the wind-blown accumulation of the gravels. The "crust" seems to me to be localized along old erosion lines. —The Sanmen age of the crust seems to me adequately established by the physiography—and perhaps even more by a study of the high gravel terraces of the northwest Ordos, which have all the characteristics of a desert crust, and are of known age.

One ticklish point still to be settled is the age of the deformed fans which build the foothills of the Nanshan, Tienshan, and Altai ranges, with respect to the "crust." The two formations are distinct[12]—southwest of Hami, the "crust" is apparently tilted locally—which would argue for a like age. But if the folded fans are really Sanmenian, as some of the fossils seem to prove, we have got to find an age for the pre-loess high terraces which can be seen in the valleys and which dissect these same fans themselves: and that becomes a complicated matter. Could there possibly be local terrace-systems related to the Pleistocene glaciation of the Tienshan?

For the last two months I have been busy editing a number of papers and maps. A study of the Chou-Kou-Tien lithic industry will come out in the next bulletin. My views are more conservative than those of Breuil. I do not believe in a systematic bone-industry at C.K.T., and still less in worked bones at Nihowan! ... A small memoir with a map of Weichang is off the press and will appear in the next Survey bulletin. I have a sketch map with another paper ready—on the distribution of Upper Palaeozoic and Mesozoic clastic sediments that have been granitized (the Khangai series, the Linnsi series, etc.). I wish that the Survey would develop the publication of this kind of map of the different formations, especially for the volcanic rocks. Another point of growing interest for me is the research and study into fissure-deposits, of the kind found at C.K.T. or Wanhsien. Young Wang,[13] whom I don't think you know, has come back from Yunnan and has found new deposits of this type near Yunnanfu. I would greatly like to make a field-trip there within two years. Grabau and Black to the contrary notwithstanding, I am convinced that the good hunting ground is there rather than in Sinkiang.

I am thinking of spending the autumn and early winter in France.

In the meantime, unless the printing of certain studies detains me, I expect to spend three or four weeks in Shansi—starting from Taiku and going straight south to the Huangho, down the east bank of the Fenho. I would much like to have had you with me. I hope that will happen some day.

Black leaves early in July on a long reconnaissance trip across Persia, Iraq, and Palestine. He should be back in Peking, like myself, in February or March.

Wong is at Nanking for a few days. He received your last letter safely.

My best remembrances to your wife,

All yours,
Teilhard

As study of the fossils progressed, it became clear that the relatively isolated position of Chou-Kou-Tien—thousands of miles from the nearest localities where other Late Cenozoic strata were known (Japan, Java, India, etc.)—ruled out any simple faunal correlation as a means of setting an exact age to the Peking man "horizon." Davidson Black realized that the Cenozoic Laboratory could attain its objectives only by extending its reconnaissances right across China and into Central Asia. At that time (before more recent finds seemed to support the theory of an East Central African root for the origin of man), the "Cradle of the Human Race" was thought to exist somewhere in the heart of the Eurasian Continent—a projection of ideas put forward in Black's study, "Asia and the Dispersal of the Primates" (1926).

Black had already made contact with authorities in India and the Middle East, as a first step in his plan to lead a Cenozoic Expedition into the mid-continent. He came to New York with Teilhard and Grabau in the summer of 1933, just before the Washington meeting of the XVIII International Geological Congress, with a view to securing from the Rockefeller Foundation approval for this project, and for a preliminary reconnaissance into West China. Though the idea appealed to members of the Board, it was still too soon after the depression for them to feel it wise to make commitments more than a year in advance. But the encouraging impression was gained that the successful results of a shorter first reconnaissance might justify repeating the major request a year later. Accordingly, while we were in Washington, Black asked me to return to China early in 1934, as Visiting Physiographer to the Rockefeller Foundation, in order to make two traverses across the country with Teilhard: the first, up the Yangtze Corridor as far as Western Szechwan; the second, along a roughly parallel line further to the north following the route I had taken from Sian to Lanchow three years previously.

The Congress itself began with registration at the Geological Society headquarters in New York. There Teilhard had just arrived from Peking, when he was warmly greeted by his friend, Pierre Pruvost of Paris, with the words, "You can't imagine, old fellow, how glad I am to see you again!"

"I feel the same way," replied Teilhard, "but for an entirely different reason."

"And what is that?"

"Because now I *know* the world is round."

After the Washington Congress, Teilhard joined "Excursion C-2," which crossed the United States in two pullmans and a baggage car coupled to a succession of trains during the nights, and left on sidings during the day while we were out in the field. The nerve center of the party was the famous Princeton University car which had been rebuilt as a mobile office and conference room, fitted with map table, blackboard, projection screen, and storage facilities for equipment, rock samples, and geological paraphernalia. The third unit of our caravanserai on wheels was a standard Pullman sleeping car with "sections" of double-deck berths and a single drawing room, the latter normally reserved for married couples. One such suite was assigned to Pierre Pruvost and his wife. The rest of us slept in section berths. At

night, all our possessions had to be repacked in our bulging suit-
cases and stowed under the seats. Late one afternoon somewhere
on the plains of Kansas, after a grilling day in the open, Teilhard
changed his shirt and looked for a place to hang his discarded
garments. Glancing ruefully at the vast spaces in the drawing
room, he drew Dr. A. Renier of Brussels aside and twitted him
for dereliction of duty in not managing things better. "Listen,
Renier, could you not have used your well-known diplomatic
gifts to better advantage and secured for us at least half a wife
apiece?"

On the night of August 10, Teilhard and I shared a cabin
overlooking Crater Lake. The next day but one, he left the
party abruptly at Eugene, Oregon, to drive back to San Francisco
with two of Dr. Ralph Chaney's students from the University
of California. Three weeks later he wrote:

University of California
Berkeley, Sept. 6, 1933

My dear George,

Before sailing for Shanghai the day after tomorrow, I want to send
you, along with some news, a last and most affectionate greeting. For
me, it has been a great joy to see you for so long in such freedom in
recent weeks. What I would wish now is that, among the many possi-
bilities that take shape before you, you manage to focus more sharply
the line that will lead you to the most fruitful life. The better I know
you, the more do I believe that you can achieve a great deal—*precisely*
because you are the most natural *intermediary* between America and
Asia. As far as possible you must sacrifice neither of the two countries
to the other—but your special value lies in the fact that you know
*both* chessboards. After spending a month in California, I leave absolutely convinced of the need, and of the magnitude of the task, which
involves "bridging the Pacific." You are one of the men most indicated
for that. Speaking confidentially, *that* interests me even more than
Black's great South Asian or trans-Asiatic project. We shall see what
future events decide. I would dream of a reconnaissance with you
through South China, and a serious contact with Japan. In any case, I
shall press Black to make use of you for detailed studies of *high* yield

in China. I shall keep you informed. Meanwhile, establish yourself in America as a base of operations. The two things ought to form a fundamental combination: —and it would be marvelous to build up something together, the two of us.

I left the C-2 party a trifle startled when Chaney pulled me off the bus and stuck me in the little Ford with his two students. But in that kind of situation a little brusqueness does no harm. Basically, I did well to push no further, but to reserve myself for California. In several weeks I have learned a great deal—both here in the laboratory, where Matthew has launched a team of enthusiastic, bright young research men: and in the field. From Eugene, I reached San Francisco by the coast route ("Redwood Highway"). Last week I did the coast range south of San Francisco, as far as the outskirts of Santa Barbara, with Camp and three other geologists. Another time I did the Mariposa-Yosemite district with a young geologist very familiar with the region. I am greatly struck by the fundamental tectonic analogies between the Mesozoic and Tertiary chains of California and those of China and Sinkiang. The Pacific acts like an immense Tarim Basin.

From another point of view, it seems to me that there is extreme confusion here regarding the Pleistocene. Younger than the folded "Pleistocene" series of the Coast Ranges—and older than the sediments with Rancho La Brea fauna—one can see everywhere (e.g., along the Eal River, north of San Francisco), traces of high terraces which seem to me thus far to be localized. . . . There is an entire physiographic history to be worked out here. If only you could come back again.[14]

Grabau has been here for two days. He is well, but seems somewhat sad—a mood that has been on the increase for the last two or three years. You know that he has decided to send fifty dollars gold per month to [his daughter] Josephine. Things will be distinctly tight at Tou Ya Tsai Hutung![15] Altogether it has been a good thing that he returned to America. You did well to help him in this.

Affectionate greetings to your wife.

Fraternally yours,
P. Teilhard

Davidson Black followed Teilhard and Grabau back to Peking and wrote me from there, formally confirming the proposal made in Washington. Much of the success of the Congress had been due to a large grant from the Penrose Bequest to the Geological Society of America. The same fund had allowed an expansion of the Society's publication program, and I was acting as scientific and literary critic in the editorial office in New York, to which I returned after the C-2 Excursion. By working overtime under pressure, it was possible to deal with a sufficient pile of manuscripts to furnish a full year's fodder for the presses well ahead of time. This allowed me to leave New York on February 25, 1934, in time to board *S.S. Malolo* at Los Angeles on March 3.

As one means of keeping touch with my family, daily "home-letters" were sent back to report progress, allay apprehension, and transmit news from friends of our Chinese days whom I met en route. Plane services were still in their infancy. Mail from Peking to New York might start for the China coast by plane, and go on by boat from Fusan or Shanghai one day, and the next travel by Trans-Siberian Express through Manchouli to Moscow and Berlin, before crossing the Atlantic from Hamburg, Cherbourg, or Southampton. More than one hundred and fifty of these informal communiqués, dated and numbered in sequence, have survived from that summer. These supplement data from field notebooks, as a basis for the account given in the pages which follow. The five-month field season fell naturally into two parts, each of which merits a separate chapter—the first devoted to the Yangtze basin, and the next to North China.

Profile of Teilhard as he appeared in the 1950s.

Teilhard with a chipmunk in Kansas.

Teilhard and Young (center) and a third member of the Chinese Geological Survey.

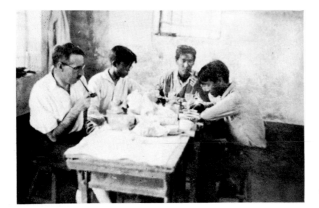

Dr. Barbour, Chia, Eddie Bien, and Pei in the field laboratory of Chou-Kou-Tien.

Teilhard examines the *Plesianthropus breccia* at Sterkfontein.

# 6

# The Yangtze Expedition

EITHER Black or Teilhard was to let me know the final plans for the Yangtze Expedition before the *Malolo* sailed or when she docked at Honolulu. But there was no letter from either of them.

The crossing as far as Hawaii was uneventful. The second day at sea, a spry 50-year-old fellow passenger asked if he might join a game of deck tennis. He said he was a Chicago writer on his way to lecture in the University of Honolulu, taking his wife on their first Pacific cruise. Later in the day, he dropped into the deck chair next to mine and chatted about his days as a cub-reporter with Scripps, Hearst, and other newsmen when he was writing about smelters, stockyards, and other facets of industrial life. He seemed pleased to note that I was two-thirds through a paperback entitled *Abraham Lincoln,* and mentioned in passing that his name was Carl Sandburg. He asked about the quest on which I was setting out, wanted to know more about Teilhard, and urged me to visit him in his hotel on Waikiki Beach to read the poems on which he was working.

When Teilhard was with the C-2 Congress Excursion at Crater Lake the previous August, discussion had turned on the lavas of the "fire-girdle of the Pacific" and its connection, if any, with the young volcanoes on the edge of Mongolia in which Teilhard had recently become interested. I had promised to raise several questions with Dr. Thomas Jagger, the vulcanologist who guarded the hearth of the Fire Goddess Pele at Kilauea on Hawaii.

I had visited him before, and on docking at Honolulu found a message asking me to cross to the southern island without delay. There being no word from Black or Teilhard indicating haste, I took the night boat to Hilo on Hawaii Island, where Dr. Jagger devoted three days to answering my questions, explaining his ideas about forecasting eruptions, and escorting me about the island.

I flew back to Oahu, to show my film on the Tennessee Valley Authority project before the Engineering Society of Honolulu, to make the circuit of the island with local geologists, and to lunch with Carl Sandburg. On the morning of Friday, March 16, I spoke by radio phone with my family in New York before boarding the *Empress of Japan* late in the day for an early sailing the next morning.

At 3:00 A.M., four hours before we were due to cast off, a radiogram from New York was brought to my cabin. It read

DAVIDSON BLACK DIED HEART YESTERDAY

The next home letter read:

*Empress of Japan*
Saturday 17 March, 6 P.M.

. . . After getting your cable, I spent all the time till we cast off trying to see whether plans should be changed. There was *no* word from Black or Teilhard at Honolulu. But the work must go on, though now without Black's long-range planning and inspired leadership. It is strange how God works. Here is epoch-making work cut short in the middle, with no one capable of carrying it on as Davy Black himself could have done. The immediate task of the summer may now be all the more significant.

I received the full cost of my travel tickets in New York. It would have been Black, rather than Ting or Wong, who might have induced me to stay on in Peking once the field season was over. Teilhard,

66

Young, and I form a self-contained unit, left to define and solve problems on our own. Black told me in Washington what he hoped for. Having cleared my desk at the Geological Society, there is nothing in New York to warrant turning in my tracks. So I go on prayerfully believing that you would agree that it is the only right course. Once the *Empress* had weighed anchor, it was too late to change, even had I wanted to. . . .

At dawn on Monday, March 27, the *Empress* threaded her way slowly up the Whangpoo River, across the Yangtze Delta, and anchored in mid-channel off the Bund, or waterfront, of Shanghai. A tender came alongside at once. A courier called my

*Dr. Barbour. (Empress of Japan)*

*I wait for you at the Custom's Jetty*

*P. Teilhard de Chardin, Dr. Sc.*

HONORARY ADVISER
TO THE CHINESE NATIONAL GEOLOGICAL SURVEY

*Teilhard*

MUSEE HOANGHO-PAIHO
TIENTSIN

name and handed me a visiting card with the scribbled message: "I wait for you at the Custom's Jetty. Teilhard."

As we neared shore, I made out a straight black figure between two shorter ones in khaki, above a blue-grey sea of coolies. It was Teilhard with Eddie Bien and C.C. Young. Over a meal at the hotel, they gave me the news, everyone talking at once. After the others left, Teilhard and I talked for two hours about the devastating effect of Black's death ten days previous.

Teilhard reported that two months earlier, V.K. Ting had

yielded to appeals from all sides that he return to public life as Director of the Academia Sinica in Nanking. J.S. Lee, who had headed the Geological Institute there for three years, had just accepted a professorship in the National University in Peking. In January, Dr. Wong Wen-hao, Director of the Geological Survey, had his skull fractured in a serious motor accident, and he had only survived by a miracle. A man of less hardy constitution would never have recovered. It was hoped that by the end of the summer he might be able to recognize people and see visitors.

A slight heart attack in January had sent Davidson Black into the hospital for five weeks' examination; this explained his failure to answer my letters of December and January. Early in March, he began to deal with correspondence again. A letter dated March 5 just missed me in Honolulu, but Teilhard brought a carbon copy. In it, Black agreed to the plan I proposed as the best use that could be made of the summer, but he had delayed confirming it until a letter I sent to J.S. Lee, as Head of the Geological Institute, led the latter to offer his cordial cooperation in any work Teilhard and I wished to do on the Lower Yangtze. This lay in the Nanking (Academia Sinica) sphere of influence, rather than that of the Geological Survey, which was still under Dr. Wong Wen-hao in Peking. Hence Black's tactful delay.

The morning on which I spoke to New York by radiophone from Honolulu, Davidson Black had gone back to his laboratory for the first time, saying that he "felt fine, and was eager to get back" to his interrupted study of the latest specimen from Chou-Kou-Tien. When Dr. Paul Stevenson, his colleague in the Anatomy Department at the P.U.M.C., entered the laboratory a few minutes later, Black was lying on the floor. Teilhard felt as if he had lost another brother.

Teilhard also brought me a letter from Dr. Roger Greene, Field Director of the China Foundation of the Rockefeller Board. He said Teilhard was to be Rockefeller representative as Acting

Director of the Cenozoic Laboratory until Black's successor was chosen. But since Teilhard's appointment had first to be announced in New York, the fact was not known to the rank and file of the Cenozoic staff. However, it must have been known to V.K. Ting, because Roger Greene was always punctilious in dealing with Chinese colleagues. Greene added that our summer field work must go ahead exactly as outlined in Black's letter to me. Sound research reports were the one thing that would guarantee continued support of the Cenozoic after the end of the year. Thereafter, discussions with V.K. Ting and Wong Wen-hao would decide the future of the Laboratory.

Teilhard felt that with Ting now tied to the Academia, Wong Wen-hao disabled, J.S. Lee in his new office at the National Survey in Peking, Grabau absorbed in his theories and more immobile than ever, and Davidson Black now gone (and to be replaced by an anthropologist able to complete Black's unfinished work in the laboratory), there remained only the two of us to tackle the problems laid out by Black as summer fare for the Cenozoic. Young and Bien would be available as field colleagues.

While awaiting the boat for Los Angeles in December 1931, I had spent a week in the Nanking District. As Teilhard was unfamiliar with the area, it was decided to begin our traverse up the Yangtze Valley by revisiting the key places on which I had previously reported. This we were glad to do in company with J.S. Lee's Institute geologists, and thus learn which, if any, of my conclusions were wrong, and see any new field evidence which had been found in the previous three years. After that, Lee himself would join us two days further up the river, in the hope of solving the problem as to whether the Lushan Range had or had not undergone glaciation.

How far we would go up the river beyond Hankow would have to depend upon what we learned on the Lower Yangtze. But we had to be back in Peking by early May, at which time a Memorial Meeting for Davidson Black was being planned. I had also promised V.K. Ting and J.S. Lee to give a series of lectures in the National University before we set out on a second east-west traverse, unless the monsoon downpours made overland travel impossible.

A letter written on arrival at Nanking described the first stage of our journey.

Nanking Hotel, Nanking
Saturday, March 31

Our start was not propitious. At Young's insistence, we postponed departure from 8 to 9 A.M. to suit the convenience of a member of the party who slept the night with relatives half-way across the Chinese city of Shanghai. We thus forfeited seats reserved on the Nanking Express, and found ourselves on a *Bummelzug* that took three hours longer. We had to sit on our baggage in the corridor all the way to Soochow and keep getting up to let peripatetic vagrants pass.

You recall the familiar scenes—mothers feeding chubby babies at their breasts: piles of baggage blocking the fairways: beggars wailing their piteous entreaties beside the tracks; hawkers on the platforms doing a brisk trade in varnished ducks, unfresh eggs, lacquered red-fruit on skewers, and sticks of sugar cane; passengers chewing dried sunflower and watermelon seeds like parakeets, and spitting out the husks—a technique I never mastered, alas!—the banter back and forth; the cheerful squalor and general irresponsibility; the white gowned car boy circulating endlessly with his dingy teapot; and the constant arguments with the harassed conductor about mislaid or non-existent tickets. It all feels so utterly natural, even after two years' absence . . .

Nanking, Monday, April 2

. . . Nanking is very different from the adolescent capital you saw two years ago. New roads run out into the country in all directions, carrying motor buses that keep time to the minute—all as badly over-loaded as any around Peking, with the central aisle filled with stand-ing passengers, baggage piled to the roof, ducks and chickens in wicker baskets, and bicycles hooked over the bumpers or slung from the roof-rails. Today we covered eighty miles at breakneck speed, without a single puncture.

The city itself is a self-conscious hive of activity. Imposing new buildings sprouting everywhere; huge military camps, hospitals, and schools staked out with surveyors' pegs in the area around the city wall; the new station a-building, with through trains to Hangchow, and the same old Blue Express now running through, Shanghai to Tientsin. Lots of eye wash, too—traffic lights that blink too fast for hand-carts and funeral catafalques to get across without snarling up traffic in four directions; airplane beacons that wink only on state occasions; silent radio masts; an astronomical observatory that gets blacked out nightly by the pall of Yangtze Delta mist; as well as windows full of tawdry geegaws and quasi-foreign imitations—"one immense monkey house" as P.T. vividly puts it. But to my mind the general appearance is one of improvement, business is thriving, and the radio over our supper table gave us world news, including what I managed to make out about the breakdown of Japanese-British negotiations in London—all reported in a high falsetto with a sing-song southern dialect, unlike our Peking mandarin. This was followed by selections from Carmen played by a Chekiang band on Chinese instruments. One felt it should have been "Madame Flutterby," rather than the Chinese idea of French music about Spain.

Until Prof. J.S. Lee arrives from Peking a week hence, the Nanking Academia geologists must keep us busy in this area. I rebelled a little at what seemed too like wasting time in padding out our first outing to see a locality that could hardly prove productive except to let Teilhard see for himself the rightness of my printed report. So for two hours I rather forced the pace with excellent results. We were already ahead of schedule, and fortunately one of the others suggested the obvious solution—and we caught the last bus back to Nanking instead of spending the night in the field. This let us clean up, change, and write up notes. Thus far, my findings of 1931 hold water; if writing the report again today, the only change would be to state categorically what I then wrote with minor qualifications. It was good to be able to start by congratulating Lee's men heartily on the soundness of their conclusions.

The delay in Lee's arrival gave Teilhard his first chance to study on the ground the Central China landscape, which thus far he knew only from the train window on his journeys between Shanghai and Tientsin. He was fascinated by the contrasts with the counterparts in Mongolia, Shansi, and the Yellow River Plain. In the south as in the north, human muscle was a primary source of power. But here canal boats, water buffalo, wheelbarrows, and sedan chairs replaced carts, oxen, mules, camels, and rickshas. The water-logged delta flats of the Yangtze are criss-crossed by a maze of dikes and canals, on which farmers pole their shallow craft, piled high with cabbages and other market garden produce.

Our second trip was into the hill country southeast of Nanking. At the end of the bus line, we left the low ground, and for half a dozen miles rode in bamboo chairs slung on poles carried shoulder high by bearers who shuffled along at a jog trot, their step timed to the bounce of the springy poles. They travelled at better than four miles an hour, with only the briefest of halts every twenty minutes. An extra runner trotted along nearby, ready at a shout to slip under the poles and take the strain to the same rhythm, replacing a fore or aft bearer, without missing a step or dropping a passenger. Teilhard pointed out that once you got over your fear that you were going to land in a paddy field, or be thrown out at each heave, you could relax at ease and fall asleep to the soothing swing of the chair. Our four bed-rolls and the supply box followed more sedately on a wheelbarrow.

Our bearers threaded their way furlong after furlong along the narrow path or causeway that wound interminably for half a dozen miles between paddy fields, before the final rise to a village where the streets were so narrow that two wheelbarrows could hardly pass abreast. Our destination was the village inn where the menage was ruled by the innkeeper's mother, a bound-footed dictator of 60 or better. She hobbled about the place keeping her hands warm by holding them over a charcoal brazier slung under her skirt from a belt of webbing around her waist—a practical form of central heating. We made a partition of trestles as a barrier to keep curious visitors at a distance—while we set up our camp cots and the survey assistant opened the commissariat box. Our guides found satisfying local food, but insisted on furnishing us with bully beef, which with boiled eggs, new bread wrapped in wax paper, tinned marmalade, and Australian butter made a banquet.

Three days later, we ferried across the Yangtze to study the rocks on the left bank. The plan had been to go north by rail from Pukow, where the Peking train leaves the river. In former days, through-passengers had to change trains and cross the river late at night, struggling not to lose their belongings in the dark. With the recent inauguration of a rail-ferry service, the train was cut into three, the dismembered head and tail being then floated across the half-mile expanse of water before being recoupled on reaching the further bank. But since there was danger in this crossing, it was felt safer to attempt it only by daylight. As a result, both north-bound and south-bound expresses were now timed to cross early in the afternoon. This meant a six-hour change of time table in both directions, and a rescheduling of all connecting trains at every junction along five hundred miles of main line. This change had been made only five weeks before and news of it had not yet filtered down to the office concerned with our movements; thus we reached the station only to learn that we would have to wait five hours on the platform, provided our train had even left Shanghai—a fact that could not be verified till the train arrived in Nanking. So instead we crossed by public ferry, and took Teilhard to the outcrops seen in 1931 and to two others found since, before returning the same way. One incident that interested him took place as we re-crossed the river. Two men, each with a pair of pigeons hanging head down, boarded the boat. The first pair were released 100 yards from the bank and flew back home. The second were not freed till the boat swung around in mid-channel. They must have already earned their pilot's wings because they flew off in a wide double spiral before taking an arrow-straight flight line for home.

We returned to Nanking and learned that Dr. Erik Norin of Uppsala had just come back to Peking from Chinese Tibet, and had been persuaded by J.S. Lee to join the projected trip up the Yangtze to Lushan. Norin's recent study of glacial features in the northwest would undergird our own conclusions about the puzzling landforms on the mountain summit which Lee thought were due to ice action.

The rest of the week was spent with the soil experts at Ginling, the Union University—James Thorp and Lossing Buck (husband of Pearl Buck)—discussing the relation of soil color to past and present climate, studying every available paragraph in English, French, and German on the shelves of the Academia Library, and going back to Shanghai to consult reports and maps not available in the capital. I also paid a visit to the Siccawei Observatory to get weather reports and information on the relative reliability of air lines in the hinterland.

When J.S. Lee's arrival was again postponed, Teilhard decided that we would have to start without him. Young had met unexplained delays in securing internal passports (*huchiao*) for Teilhard and himself, though I got mine without any trouble. When the other two passes finally came, we took a river steamer, appropriately named *Kiang-An* (River Peace), as far as Anking, after leaving word for Lee to meet us at Kiu-kiang, a day further upstream.

On the Yangtze, aboard *S.S. Kiang-An*
Wednesday, April 11

Up at 4:30 A.M., we learned that the *Kiang-An* had docked, so made the six-mile ricksha run across the length of Nanking to the wharf in fast time. We got on board through the crush of laden coolies, sleeping passengers, and heaps of goods on every inch of deck space; but found clean, spotless cabins, large windowed dining room and lounge—even a piano, and that in tune!

We are sailing up a grey overhung Yangtze, with no visible geology except the silt terrace. Pierre is keeping a weather eye open for rock outcrops on the banks, while I write. We reach Anking tomorrow, long before dawn, go into the field all day, and board another river steamer at night.

Aboard *S.S. Hsin-ning,* between Anking and Kiukiang
Friday, April 13

Every inch of deck space is filled with soldiers bound for camp at Kiu-kiang. The morning went to long-distance study of the banks through binoculars. Twenty minutes ago, we passed a queer island hill rising almost vertically out of the water, like the famous classical paintings of Chinese artists which to our eyes look fantastic. And yet when you see them, they are so striking, that you cannot blame painters

Rock Island Temple

for wanting to remember them. Teilhard was delighted with this one. "It must be the prototype of hundreds of designs in silk, paint and pottery."

Kiu-kiang, Saturday, April 14

The most beautiful sight of the day yesterday was when we over-hauled a covey of boats beating up against the current in a cross wind,

and making surprising headway, beneath a pagoda perched on a terrace commanding the river.

Kiu-kiang, Monday, April 16

While waiting for Lee's boat to arrive, Teilhard suggested that we walk along the bund, and study the shipping notices we had passed when disembarking. As far as Ichang, boats sail up the meandering Yangtze by night as well as by day. Exact positions of the shifting channels between the sand bars become very important after dark, and pilots steer by beacon lights either on the banks or set on floating buoys. One notice read: "Due to shift of channel, buoy No. 243 has been moved and now stands at bearing 265° from the next downstream."

Larger notice boards, visible by telescope from any captain's bridge, give in huge figures the present depth in feet of the main channel at Anking, Kiu-kiang, and Hankow, so that boats of less than 14-feet draught know it is deep enough to proceed safely in the dark. In the gorges above Ichang, all craft must anchor overnight, since eddies and reefs make pools and rapids which determine a river boat's choice of passage, and vary sharply with the changing volume and swiftness of the flow at different water levels. The "Yangtze Pilot" gives details of these Scylla and Charybdis risks at each level of the water. The river pilots have an uncanny sense of feel for the channel, as they worm their way up against the flood.

On Lee's arrival, the party was complete, and early next day we set out, all six of us—Lee, Yu, Young, Norin, Teilhard, and myself—with the Academia attendant and our baggage, on a chartered bus. This broke down with "an upper respiratory infection" two miles outside Kiu-kiang. The delay gave a welcome chance to look at the rocks, and get warm by walking, as the morning was very cold. . . . When the bus overtook us, we drove to the foot of the mountain where we bargained for sedan chairs, and started up the steps of the 3,000-foot stairway. I have a cinefilm strip of Teilhard and the rest of the party, trying to look at ease with their feet almost as high as their heads. Two miles from the summit, we left the chairs to climb for three hours on a ridge above the snow line.

The Fairy Glen Private Hotel at Kuling (altitude 3,500 feet) is owned by a Scot, who must once have lived on the Lamlash Road in Arran down the Clyde. The ground on the Lushan mountain tops is as it ought to be—moor with large blocks of schist scattered about on the soaking earth, with rivulets of clear water trickling over boulders in broad saddle-like valleys. It was not hard to see why Lee wanted to give them a glacial explanation. We climbed to a peak 3,800 feet above the Yangtze and Poyang Lake far below us.

Valley S. of Kuling on Lushan from ridge E. of Fairy Glen

The ridges rise abruptly from the plain. The scenery is magnificent—a sketch shows the top 2,000 feet of the ridge across from the Lion's Leap.

The lower slopes were as green as Ceylon or Hawaii, except for bare bedrock exposures and occasional brown or yellow patches marking landslides. At one point, a hermit had built a small house and shrine, using slabs of local stone. A round hole with a platform in front served as door, window, and chimney. Lee had known a Chinese gentleman in the valley below who was so impressed with the hermit's holiness that he brought him bread daily for a year. At the moment we passed it, just below the Pinnacle of Lion's Leap, the place was hung with icicles and snow, like a Christmas tree.

77

Snow on the
Hermit's Shrine
below Lion's Leap

On the fourth day, we found a good night's lodging in a sacred grove at Pai-lou Tung (Grotto of the White Faun). Here stands a shrine to Chu Hsi, the chief magistrate of Nankanfu in the Sung Dynasty (Xth Century), the "First Chinese Geologist." He had noted fossils in the rocks high on the mountains and made the comment that the sea must once have stood at that level. Rest was good after twenty-one miles of rough going on narrow paths, five of them on steps down a mountain 3,400 feet high. The lower hill slopes are painted with mauve, red, and deep yellow rhododendrons and lilies in flower.

Teilhard was interested that Ferdinand von Richthofen came here in 1882—a fact I had dredged from *China* in the library in Shanghai.

A beautiful and amusing day provided only twists in the main geological question which we had been called in to answer. It looked as if the crucial evidence had been destroyed by the passage of time, and we saw we might have to leave the problem unsolved till someone else could spend months in the area. Much of Lee's "evidence" was unconvincing, but he had found one of the hardest things to account for that it had been my fortune to see. A mass of material, which it was hard to explain as other than glacial, exists, but without ice having left any of its usual "earmarks" on the landscape. Teilhard and Norin were just as puzzled. But it will be my task to write the verdict . . .

On return to Kiu-kiang, we said goodbye to J.S. Lee and Yu, who went back to Nanking.

Another day on the Yangtze brought us to the huge river port at the mouth of the Han. Our first experience of Hankow was not a happy one. Everyone had told us to stay at the "German

Hotel" close to the river, since its owner held to Bavarian standards of cleanliness and cuisine. The Chinese word for Deutschland being *Teh-kuo* (Land of Virtue) led to the hotel being referred to as *Teh-kuo Fantien.* It no doubt also boasted a more fancy name—Grand or Imperial Kaiserhof—for use on menus and stationery. While waiting to land, we were looking over the rail of the *Kiang-shun* at the touts and hotel boys soliciting business. One particularly villainous looking fellow had a card in his hatband clearly reading TEH-KUO FANTIEN. Young signaled to him, and in a minute they had agreed on something. Not liking the look of things, I protested to Teilhard that I was sure the representative of any German hotel would wear some kind of uniform, or at least the white cap of a commodore or band leader. Also, he would surely understand a few words of German, while this disreputable character did not. But Teilhard replied that Young spoke Chinese, knew what we wanted, and *could not* be mistaken.

By the time we reached the bund, a cavalcade of rickshas had been engaged, with our baggage piled high in the first two. As we mounted, the convoy pulled off quickly, Young in the lead, Teilhard next, Norin behind him, myself at the tail. We started north, straightaway from the river, at a fast clip. After a quarter of a mile, one of the bedding-rolls fell off on the filthy street. I shouted again in protest, but Teilhard just waved ahead, and my voice was lost in the street noises. After we had gone a mile in the wrong direction, and were in the heart of the Chinese city, getting farther and farther from the Yangtze, the cortege suddenly pulled up in front of THE ORIENTAL HOTEL – TEH-KUO FANTIEN, an unsavory-looking erection on the edge of the red-light district.

By the time I could dismount, all our material had been pounced upon and carried upstairs to a large room at the far end of the corridor, with whitewash flaking off walls and obviously not cleaned for a generation. It was furnished with one rattan settee, three broken chairs, and a couple of red tables, and lit by a single fly-specked bulb with a dangling strip of fly-paper attached. Husks of chewed watermelon seeds had been swept into corners; the door would not latch, and there were no sanitary arrangements. Each time any of us left the room, painted ladies appeared at the doors of cubicles down the corridor. (There was some humor in its name not being "Hotel of the Land of Easy Virtue"—even though it used Teilhard's Chinese name, Teh.) We were evidently to be the talk of the town. The establishment provided no food, but the host sent down the street to a restaurant, which an hour later delivered a nest of containers with tepid soup, rice, and unidentifiable garden produce. We set up our cots in a square, and were glad that the food supply box brought from Nanking was not quite empty.

Norin was in favor of paying for the night, and moving at once to the real German Hotel. But Teilhard, while admitting that "Young might perhaps have made a mistake," pointed out that to change our abode now would mean too much loss of face for Young. So we turned in for the night after pulling our cots away from the windows, stowing our valuables in our sleeping sacks, and barricading the door with all the movable furniture. We piled it high in an unstable heap that would topple with a deafening crash if anyone tried to open the door. No one slept much that night. Next day, Teilhard remarked that he envied my working knowledge of the language, and wished he were not "at the mercy of circumstance" in a land where saving face matters so much. But he was still convinced it was an "honest mistake."

After breakfast, Teilhard was persuaded to ask at the French Consulate for a French consular travel permit, since Young mentioned that the Chinese one he had brought from Nanking did not go beyond Hankow. The Vice-Consul proved to be a man Teilhard had met in Abyssinia. My own *laissez passer* could hardly have been more extensive, since it listed every province in the country by name, with the single exception of Honan, which we were not planning to visit then. A covering letter noted, "It will be seen that your pass has not been made valid for Honan Province owing to the presence there of banditry." The clause was inserted by the Chinese Government to safeguard itself. All other areas were reported quiet.

The next move was not clear. Norin had only a week of freedom left, and Young wanted to go back and finish writing a paper in Peking. He did not seem to relish the thought of going farther upstream. It was not quite as when Teilhard, through ignorance of the language, had to leave all arrangements in Young's hands. The latter seemed to feel that a trip to the northwest later would be more rewarding; besides, it would be across his own province of Shansi, where the inhabitants spoke a dialect he understood better. Since there was no point in alienating Young with whom Teilhard was going to continue to work, we decided to visit a hill locality near Chikungshan north of Hankow. Here we hunted for further evidence of glaciation, but without success. We saw all that was necessary, but the absence of any deposits of recent age made Teilhard and Young accept the suggestion, highly applauded by Norin, of catching the next train to Peking. On the train, we completed a report on the Lushan problem. Our conclusions did not agree with those of J.S. Lee, but his courtesy at Kuling and his entire conduct throughout had been so admirable that we were anxious to leave no ill feeling. This made wording our report difficult, since Lee had already prepared for the press a scientific address on the subject.

Before we reached Peking, the following letter went home.

Train to Peking, Wednesday, April 25

P.T. and I have worked out the following plan. The Memorial gathering for Black is to be on 11 May. All three of us have to speak, and it gives us an official reason for returning from Hankow. We shall go in

81

the field again the following week. Meanwhile, there are my lectures at Yenching and Pei-ta, a three-day visit to Chou-Kou-Tien, and a lot of preparatory study to be done, as well as friends to be seen. There is also the problem of a map project to pinpoint the critical localities where future work will have to be done in later years. Pierre had left Peiping within five days of Black's death and before Roger Greene had studied in detail the Cenozoic affairs to give him any idea of the budget available for the summer . . .

In Peking, three days later, I spoke with Roger Greene, who reported what was in his letter received at Shanghai. It would, of course, be almost impossible to find a successor to Black with all the latter's variety of gifts, and his understanding of Oriental backgrounds and psychology.

The next day, I saw V.K. Ting, who first said that he had spoken with Hsieh, the Acting Director of the Survey, and that the latter had decided on a plan, which with "three minor changes"—which it seems any director has to insist upon, in order to underline his status—was an exact repetition of what had been proposed when Black spoke to me in Washington ten months earlier. Ting also explained the cause of the costly behavior of Dr. Young. The latter had seen, in Greene's appointment of Teilhard, a move by the Rockefeller interests to take over control of everything in the Cenozoic, as soon as Black was gone. Ting assured me everything was now all right and that Young had "expressed regret for any misunderstanding," and guaranteed that his non-cooperativeness was a thing of the past; Young's earlier insistence upon returning to Peking had been, he said, "largely diplomatic." All the unhappy incidents of the trip seemed to fit in with this explanation.

Three days at Chou-Kou-Tien gave us a chance to study the new cave finds, but contributed no new knowledge in the physiographic field. In fact, upon reaching Peking, I found that the report I had just placed in their hands added nothing of importance to a forgotten memorandum that Miss Hempel produced from the files, and which I had given Black in May 1931. I also visited Dr. Wong Wen-hao for half an hour, and found him making an amazing recovery. One side of his face had been crushed, but his brain was functioning again, apparently normally.

Teilhard asked me, while in Peking, to visit a friend of his, Nirgidma de Torhout, a Mongolian princess he had met in Sinkiang when the Citroën Expedition was held up at Urumchi. She wanted information on lecturing in America, and had just received a letter from the previous American ambassador, offering to arrange her tour. So I suggested to J.P. Marquand, a fellow passenger on the *Empress of Japan,* who had meanwhile reached Peking, that he might invite us both to dinner. This would give him a unique chance to get the kind of local color he was seeking for his *Saturday Evening Post* stories, and let her profit from his knowledge of lecture-bureau techniques in New York. She was said to be the only highly cultured Mongol woman with international knowledge. She spoke English with a feeling for words, and having been at a convent school in France or Belgium, talked French with a perfection which, according to Teilhard, might have been taken as a model in the most critical school of Parisian French. And since she was currently writing a history of the Mongolian Rebellion of 1912, the high point of our conversation was her clear-cut analysis of the virtues and defects of her own race, her intense pride in Mongolia, and her scathing criticism of the Chinese, racially and individually—all given with a Parisian lightness of touch that was a constant surprise. She might have stepped out of a novel. Teilhard had touched her life, as he did that of so many others, by his conversations with her in Outer Mongolia on the meaning of life, and of God's part in the universe.

Another instance of Teilhard's impact upon those he met deserves recording here. A member of the British community in Peking had recently suffered a tragic bereavement. She had

83

grown up in the austere tradition of Scottish Presbyterianism, but her own faith seemed to offer her little solace. Thinking that the comfort she sought might be found within the Catholic Church, she spoke to Teilhard of her anguish in this period of trial. They talked for some hours before Teilhard said to her, "My child, for myself, I could never be anything but a Catholic. But for you it would be all wrong. Within your own church there is the comfort and the love that you need. But you have been content to live only on the surface of things. Go home and *really learn* what your church has to say. You will find there the comfort and strength you seek."

The primary purpose of the Yangtze Expedition as proposed by Davidson Black was twofold: first, to learn what we could about the stages through which the landscape of Central China had reached its present relief, and thus be able to compare its evolution with that of North China; second, to visit all accessible places from which fossils of recent geological age were known to have come. Together, the two undertakings should help to confirm our ideas as to Peking man's antiquity, and throw light on his geographic and climatic environment. It was also hoped that we might bring back the fossil bones of one or two animal-types new to science.[16] Teilhard fully saw the importance of the reconnaissance in the over-all plan worked out by Black the summer before his death, and heartily concurred in it.

What was planned as a continuous traverse from Shanghai to the alpine front beyond the Red Basin of Szechwan, had been interrupted even before the first half of our task had been completed. But the forced intermission at Peking had given us a useful respite before we tackled the Upper Yangtze. Experience on the Lower Yangtze had proved that we needed to be more mobile than was possible with a large party. In any case, the Academia geologists were back in Nanking, J.S. Lee had to supervise the building program at Pei-ta, and Norin had gone home to Sweden.

On the night of Sunday, May 13, Teilhard and I looked in to say *au revoir* to Grabau, before meeting Young at the Hankow Express, on which I had reserved a sleeping compartment. Our baggage was piled to the ceiling on the empty upper berth, and we were in our bunks with the lights off to discourage intruders, when the conductor entered to tell us that he had no berth for "a third foreigner," because of two army officers, each of whom wanted a compartment to himself. Fortunately, the "foreigner" proved to be Gunther Köhler, a German civil engineer on his way to complete a study for the Yellow River Commission. Young having studied in Munich, talk was mostly in German, which rather left Teilhard out of the discussion; but after Köhler left the train at the Yellow River bridge, four hundred miles down the line, I relayed the gist of what he had said. In any case, it was mostly a matter of groins, berms, footings, and spillways, in which Teilhard was not the least interested: Köhler had nothing to say about the higher reaches of the Yellow River between Shansi and Shensi. Another night and three hundred miles later, we reached Hankow and went to the real "Hotel of the Land of Virtue," where our German host and his wife made us welcome.

The next day, we lunched with the French Vice-Consul whom Teilhard had previously met, and then we ferried across the Yangtze to Wuhan, where a university car took us to a convocation at which Young and I were to speak. A heavy downpour made us glad to accept an offer of beds for the night, and we turned in, hoping that the good weather had not broken for the season.

Much of the following day was spent at the River Pilot's office, and the next night we boarded the *Changsha* west bound. The river looked exquisite in the gloaming. Pale sails would appear and vanish without a sound, like silent ghosts. A string of

85

gunboats with flags of all nations—though predominantly Chinese—added to the color. We cast off at 9:00 P.M.

For navigational purposes, masters of steam vessels distinguish three main divisions of the navigable half of the great river's 3,500 miles. 1) The *Lower Yangtze,* from the tide water up to the mouth of the Han River at Hankow; 2) the *Middle Yangtze,* from that point to Ichang, at the portal of the gorges; and 3) the *Upper Yangtze,* from Ichang to Chungking, the last

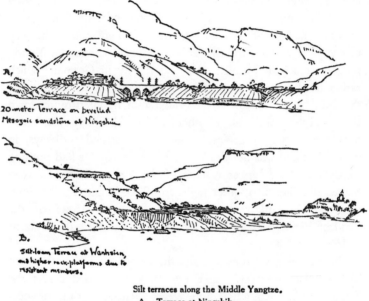

Silt terraces along the Middle Yangtze.
A. Terrace at Ningshih
B. Terrace at Wanhsien

port of any size below Pingshan, which is the upper limit for steam boats. Above Pingshan, the valley is too narrow, steep-walled, and strewn with reefs and rapids for regular river traffic. This threefold division is essentially a practical one, based upon the depth of draught of vessels which can ply safely on the main channels without grounding at various stages of high and low water. But as a geologist, Teilhard recognized only *two* major units, each of which was subdivisible into several stretches: a youthful "*upper river,*" where trenching is still in progress since the river fills its channels to depths varying locally by as much as 200 feet in the rainy season; and second, a mature "*lower river,*" along the silt-choked chain of depressions between Ichang and the sea, where for several million years the current has kept re-shifting its alluvium in wide meandering curves across the flood-plain.

The frontier between these two types of scenery lies at Ichang, three hundred miles above Hankow. Hence, our first three days out of Hankow differed little from what we had been looking at on the Lower Yangtze all the way from Nanking—a monotonous series of snake-like bends carved in the sand and silt of an endless plain, with steep walls on the outside of each curve and shelving "slip-off slopes" on the opposite bank. At four points on its lower course, the "meander belt" of the Yangtze swings a little to the north or south of its general easterly direction of flow. At these elbows, the river takes in major tributaries on the left or right bank. At times, the featureless horizon is broken by higher flat-topped platforms, clearly the remains of older flood-plain levels. Bedrock is completely buried except at one or two places where the river has swung from the axis of the depression against a confining buttress of bedrock, as at Kiukiang. All of this ends dramatically at Ichang, as abruptly as do the Great Plains of North America where they abut the Rocky Mountain Front behind Denver and Colorado Springs.

Scottish Mission, Ichang
Monday, May 21

We reached Ichang at five last night. As the boat cannot warp to the bund, but anchors in midstream, we let the first rush of passengers find their way ashore on sampans that clung to the ship like leeches. Long before the anchor was dropped, venturesome sampan owners were out in mid-channel waiting with long bamboo boat hooks for the steamer to come past. As it did, half a dozen strokes of an oar or *yu-lou* brought a sampan alongside, out shot a boat hook, and there was a shout. Either the hook caught a stanchion of the *Changsha,* and with a jerk that shook all on board, they were yanked along in tow; or it missed its mark, and went scraping along the side of the vessel, grabbing for anything that promised a purchase. Three sampans made such false grabs before the first lucky one caught hold. At once, others tried to latch onto *it,* and in an instant we were in the middle of an armada of sampans. With a blast on the whistle, the propeller was stopped and reversed. By the time the *Changsha* had drifted downstream far enough for the anchor to take hold on the bottom, she had twenty sampans, pushing, shouting, and bumping each other to nudge alongside. The boatmen must have strong wrists, since for every sampan that actually gaffed us, two more hooked to its tail, against the drag of the current. Every now and then, something would give way, and boats drifted off downstream until the lucky ones could belay their painters round a spar or bollard of the ship. One sampan came to pieces in the fray, its front stem pulled bodily out by the drag of the struggling mass—it went downstream in a flash, while the four others that had been hooked to it tried to extricate themselves. We never saw what happened to the luckless owner of the foundered craft.

When it came our turn to debark, it was an easy job, but we had to clamber across the slippery thwarts of four intervening sampans to reach the one whose enterprising coolies had made off with our baggage. Once safely on the bund, we had cached our belongings and were walking off towards the Red Cross flag of the hospital, when three ladies came up. They proved to be from the Church of Scotland Mission, and said that Miss Moore, to whom I had written, was expecting all three of us. They were actually on their way to evening service, so I hurried Teilhard and Young off to the mission residence to settle in, and went back to good old Psalter tunes with Chinese words, and a sermon by the Rev. Andrew Tocher, formerly of Edinburgh, and the gallant man who rescued a ship captain from river bandits several months ago. My pilot was a doctor who had studied medicine under my father, and dined in our home in 1908!

We have had my usual good luck in preparing for the three days at Ichang. An introduction from the Customs Commissioner's launch, complete with a Yangtze river pilot, the company of the Upper River Inspector himself, and, for good measure on the political side, a guide who is in with the local factions and knows all that is happening! So we spend tomorrow at Nantou, just inside the gorges, looking at the famous layer in which boulders carry striations that can only be explained as due to glaciation in a pre-Cambrian Ice Age 600 million years ago; the next day we go up the north bank, paralleling the river route of tomorrow; the third day we hope to solve the riddle of the red Ichang conglomerate. Then, up the gorges to Chungking. We have all the help we could ask, thanks to the friendliness of those with whom a common homeland makes a real bond. It is wonderful to sleep in such homelike surroundings as the Scottish Mission.

There are no foothills in front of the mountain at Ichang. Instead, terraces of sand and silt, extending gently back to the flood-plain, give place suddenly to a steep-walled gorge, cut into upturned layers of limestone. These strata are arched up steeply over a core of granite, which had been squeezed into place and hardened well before the dawn of life in the planet.

Whereas, for the final thousand miles from Ichang down to the sea, the river falls less than an inch and a half per mile, its gradient is more than a foot per mile for the next three hundred and sixty miles on to Chungking. The reason for this contrast is that above Ichang the river is still incising its channel into resistant bedrock. The river's effectiveness as a graving tool alters from point to point with the "competence" of the rock layers. One result is that the depth of water in the channel varies at different places from 36 feet to as much as 200 feet, plaguing the pilot with violent eddies and current changes as the level rises and falls. For the reach below the head of the great Wushan Gorge, the walls ascend precipitously, except where side streams come in. Above Wushan, the landscape is less rugged, since it is etched in softer strata lining the floor of the Red Basin of Szechwan. There, the formations are "nested" like a stack of shallow plates, across the southern edge of which the Yangtze has cut its channel down like a band-saw to its present depths.

Since Chinese sailboats cannot tack up-current against a headwind coming straight down the gorge, they have to be

89

manoeuvred by long oars or else pulled upstream by "trackers," who go ashore and haul on long bamboo hawsers harnessed over their shoulders. The banks are scored horizontally with walk ways, worn by the feet of hundreds of teams of men, who over

Terraces below Ichang.

Field sketch below Chinlingchi.

the centuries have strained at their ropes close to water level. Projecting plinths and buttresses are grooved with the notches which generations of trackers have worn as they warped their craft foot by foot slowly up river.

In places, the limestone walls rise vertical. With the river filling the canyon from wall to wall, there is no room left for the narrowest foot path on either bank. At one point, a gallery is actually chiselled into the rock face, 50 feet above the flood level. In disturbed times, bandits shoot with impunity from the top of the rock walls at boats in the canyon below. For this reason, the windows on the captain's bridge were shielded by huge steel plates, hinged like the storm dead-lights fitted over portholes near the Plimsoll line on ocean-going vessels. Late in the day, one bullet spat against the upperworks of the *Changsha,* but the officers decided it was just a practice shot fired for *joie-de-vivre* by some enthusiast on the rocks above us. The sailors did not even trouble to take off the canvas cover to load the swivel field-piece in the stern.

The *Changsha* had a bad reputation, of which we fortunately did not know. Otherwise, we might have taken another boat that was to leave Ichang later the same day. This would have meant missing three particularly fine ship's officers, all under 30, and all from Clydeside. Besides a large Union Jack amidships on each side of the boat, two large eyes were painted on the prow, like those on the coastal junks, since, as one helmsman put it, "Boat him no have eye, him no can see. Him no see, no can go."

Chungking lies three hundred and sixty miles upstream from Ichang, the first ninety mainly through magnificent gorges. These end near Wushan, where the tough layers of limestone plunge underground and give place to softer strata that have eroded back into flaring valleys. Even these are magnificently impressive, especially when seen at the bends with the higher peaks rising behind to 2,000 feet above river level. River steamers can anchor safely only at half a dozen places. We spent the night anchored off Wushan, just above the gorges. It was still light when we arrived, so Teilhard, Young, and I rowed ashore to see the geology. Teilhard was especially interested in a stand of tung trees, cultivated for the oil that forms the base of varnish.

We were up again at five, to watch the boat anchor. After a stretch of flaring valley, the river turned abruptly north, cutting through a last anticline of tough limestone, to frame the famous Windbox Gorge, with sheer walls that hold secrets still un-revealed to the geologist. At one point, a zigzag line of two-inch holes goes up the perpendicular rock face. It is supposed that they were chiselled out to hold bamboo pegs for steps to a

91

ledge high on the cliff. But today, the holes stop suddenly half-way up the face, slabs of rock having since flaked off, carrying their secret with them. Another mystery is the presence of a number of coffins wedged in narrow clefts 100 feet above the river, on a cliff-face that could hardly be climbed with a rope, much less reached by man loaded with a heavy coffin.

The second night, the *Changsha* anchored at Wanhsien, the largest port city between Ichang and Chungking. We had already planned to stop there on the return journey, and dared not delay our slow up-river progress, lest we be caught by monsoon rains that were due any day. So we stayed on board with the same friendly ship's company all the way to Chungking. My field book for the entire three hundred and sixty miles above Ichang is filled with notes on the character and "attitude" of the strata building the valley walls, and on the size and height of the terraced inlays of sediment, on which the village port communities were perched. Some pages are crowded with sketches of townlets, pagodas, and camel-back bridges, that were passed as soon as they were sighted. Teilhard looked over the taffrail or borrowed my field glasses to study the features of the rock bedding, while I alternated between my Leica and cine-Kodak, as a means of recording details which flashed past too quickly for written notes. The ship's officers amplified the data given in Captain Plant's famous *Handbook for the Guidance of Shipmasters on the Ichang-Chungking Section of the Yangtze River.*

The *Changsha* dropped anchor off Chungking on Tuesday, May 29, in perfect weather. Teilhard abruptly read me a note from an old friend in Chengtu who wanted to see him, and this added a personal reason for going one day beyond Chungking—something I hoped might be possible. It would have been ridiculous to be so near and not get to the center of the Red Basin, as Black intended. I had even offered to put up the funds without success. Apparently, the Chinese members of the Cenozoic Laboratory thought it would be a waste of time and money. Now Teilhard proposed it out of a clear sky and so it was decided.

We landed by sampan at the foot of the stone stairway that climbed 200 feet up the cliff-face. We then separated, Teilhard going to the Catholic Mission, Young to a friend in the city, and I to a huge cliff-house where transients were given hospitality by Canadian hosts. The next day was devoted to seeking information as to how to reach Chengtu, calibrating my aneroid against known elevations determined by the River Commission, and condensing our belongings. On the morning of June 4, Teilhard and I set out at 6:30, but without Young who refused to come because his Survey orders said nothing about going beyond Chungking.

Fortunately, the road was posted with milestones, because the speedometer of the decrepit car—the only one we could find in Chungking—was no more reliable than its tires. These had to be patched three times on the one hundred and seventeen-mile run to Yung-chuan; the delays did, however, give us a chance to hunt fossils while the patches dried and to study the tinted sandstone which lines the Red Basin. From dozens of observations made at as many stops, it was possible later to piece together a coherent geological story. In all, we covered two hundred and eighty miles to Chengtu. Our host there was Dr. Georges Béchamp, Director of the French Medical Mission and a long-time friend of Teilhard, who lived in a large compound near the hospital. During his ten years as French Consul for the province, Béchamp had become a mine of information, regional and international. The latter derived from the short-wave nightly newscasts of Radiodiffusion Paris.

At the library of West China Union University, I found that a member of the science faculty, Dr. Daniel Dye, was interested in geology and ready to guide our car the next day to the farthest point we were to reach, outside the portal to Chinese Tibet, at Kuanhsien. This lies forty miles northwest of Chengtu where the Min River debouches from the foothills of the Chinese Alps. Since the third century B.C., this river has been responsible for the renowned fertility of the entire basin. Each spring farmers repair the dikes that divert water into channels which deliver it to a fan-like system of distributaries. These irrigate the district and deposit an annual layer of fertile soil. Dr. Dye had found Han Dynasty coins (c. 200 B.C.) buried 20 feet below ground level.

On our brief visit to Kuanhsien, we saw the piers of the famous bamboo "swinging bridge" (just above the flumes) which had not been repaired since it was burned down by bandits two years earlier. Just outside the Kuanhsien city gates that mark the frontier of civilization, we met mules and yaks on their way down from the mountains. My camera caught Teilhard in his pith helmet and khaki uniform walking down the main street, looking at the knives and trinkets laid out in the market to catch the eye of the swarthy men from the hills. The following day being Sunday, Teilhard said mass for the hospital staff—a rare event for the expatriated French and Belgian nursing sisters.

We left Chengtu at dawn Monday in order to avoid retracing our outward-bound route back to the Yangtze. Instead, we went east and then south, and reached Chungking at dusk. The following morning, we sailed on the *Min hsien* and made fast time down river to reach Wanhsien in daylight. One incident there is described by C.C. Young in a letter to Claude Cuènot.[17] Arriving late in the day, we found the town so crowded that no room could be found in the only hotel we knew of. I had friends in the Socony Company compound, while Teilhard was bound for the Catholic Mission. Since Young was disappointed at not securing a hotel room, Teilhard suggested he go to the Mission with him. On arrival, according to Young, they were greeted with suspicion and housed in makeshift quarters for the night; but on returning two days later, they were treated as distinguished guests. As I recall it, the contretemps was in no way due, as Young suggests, to Teilhard's lack of recent practice in spoken Latin—though admittedly his Gallic pronunciation was unlike the Gaelic Scots variety that the local missionary favored. The reason was more likely that to any Szechwanese, Young's Northern Chinese provincial mandarin sounded as queer as it had to the down-river boatmen. In addition, Dr. Young's drooping eyelid so biased one side of his face that he was to undergo surgery the week we got back to Peking. Naturally, the missionary did not know what to make of two men in military khaki, telling such an improbable tale—one was clearly a foreigner, and the other, though a native, had difficulty establishing his credentials. However, all ended well, because when we got back later from a long two days in the field, we were treated

Falls at Wanhsien above discordant junction due to differential erosion. Natural bridge in foreground is eroded beneath resistant stratum of cross-bedded sandstone.

with honor—the mission Father having meanwhile wired to Chengtu, and learned that Teilhard *had* been there, and that even his odd-looking companions were to be trusted.

The following day was devoted to studying the rocks along the "hanging tributary" with its scenic waterfall and picturesque bridge, and to trying to explain the platform on which the settlement was perched. On Saturday, June 9, we left Wanhsien by chair, with a military escort, and went several miles up river on the left bank. We then crossed to the south bank in a sampan owned by a sturdy mother who manoeuvred her craft with a stern oar, her baby tied to her back, while she gave our guard her frank opinion of all soldiers.

Teilhard was aiming for the southern counterpart of the north bank tributary which enters at Wanhsien. He had heard that a limestone ridge at its headwaters was the reputed source of "dragon-bones" sold in river-port drug shops all the way down to Hankow. These bones might either be of the same geological age as the strata in which they were included as fossils, or lie in caverns or solution cavities dissolved in limestone much more ancient than the animals they once belonged to—as had been the case with the Chou-Kou-Tien trove. From the known age of the rocks we were looking at, we judged that the latter was the situation in the area ten miles south of Wanhsien. The only halt in the afternoon was at Wan-cheng, the village that made all the pottery for the district. A coarse Jurassic sandstone with a high per cent of weathered feldspar was ground in a mill powered by a water wheel, until it was fine enough to have the clay flushed out from the quartz sand. After the clay settled, it was partially dried before being shaped on a potter's wheel, and finally fired in local kilns.

We pushed on for the night to Yen-Ching-Kou (Salt Well Gap) where the water from wells drilled in the Ming Dynasty (c. 1600 A.D.) still tasted saline. The next morning, we climbed 1,200 feet to the top of the ridge, which suddenly began to show the "karst" features of limestone terrain, with pockets of reddish earth filling circular "sinks" in bedrock. Some of these terra-cotta plugs were shallow, while others filled deep funnel-holes. In the winter season, when there is no work in the fields, the local farmers dig down to depths of 200 feet and bring up from

96

the bottom of these holes a few handfuls of fossils which are then sold by the catty (a measure of one and a half pounds) to drug merchants. Early in the spring, the farmers shovel the dirt back and mark the spot for further treatment next year. The day we were there, the only thing brought up was the broken jaw of a *Stegodon* (a primitive elephant) with an unworn tooth still in its socket. Teilhard's identification of this Pliocene elephant showed that the age of the giant pitfall was consistent with the history we had worked out for the rest of the region. From the bottom of the valley, it had not been possible to decide between alternative explanations for certain crest-line features in the gorge district, and the visit to the fossil pits gave only a partial answer to the question.

On arrival at Wanhsien, we were treated like distinguished visitors at the Mission. Shortly after arrival, I went to the Socony residence and learned that a Chinese National Airways seaplane leaving the next day had vacant seats as far as Ichang. But since Young had an aversion to flying, Teilhard decided he would stay with him and the Cenozoic baggage, which now included a heavy box of specimens. They therefore boarded a boat at dawn, while I waited for the afternoon plane, which reached Ichang at 5:00 P.M. They had arrived earlier and I was obliged to overtake them as they went out on foot again to examine the left bank a mile downstream. The question at issue was the precise date of the warping of the earth's crust which had transformed the landscape by pushing up the highlands, while permitting the sagging of the basins and depressions drained by the great river.

Throughout the journey, we had been phenomenally lucky with the weather—a record low temperature of 65° one evening at Wanhsien. Chengtu had been so drenched that we were the first to get through after the roads dried. Ichang had had heavy rains during our absence up river, but dried the day before we got back. Similarly, although my pilot had had bad weather all the way up river, our flight could not have been clearer.

We got back to Peking on June 18. The next four weeks went to drafting a report on our ideas about the Yangtze, interspersed with pleasing contacts with former colleagues and friends.

Peking, June 29

After graduation ceremonies at Yenching, Leighton[18] insisted I lunch with the commencement speaker, H.H. Kung.[19] I sat beside the Chinese minister to the Court of St. James, across the table from Dr. Kung himself. Kung was taking a group of friends up to his school at Taiku in Shansi. He had read what I had written about Shansi geology, and asked about the loess.

Two days later, Dr. Kung's secretary brought a letter inviting me to go in his plane to Shansi. This coincided with the days Young was to be in the hospital for his eye, and filled the interval before we were due to start out again. It also gave an unexpected chance to settle the final point which Davidson Black had asked me to verify. Teilhard had been right in his analysis of the Fenho Valley, and it was satisfactory to have this unexpected chance to confirm it. A giant thirty-passenger Curtis Wright took eighteen of us to Taiyuan, where we were guests of the Governor, Yen Hsi-shan. Then we went on to Taiku by the road along which Nystrom had taken Teilhard and me in 1928. Dr. Kung showed us all over his vast family headquarters which covered an acre of courtyards. Many of these have exquisitely painted wooden carvings over the doors, of a delicacy not used for such decorations even in imperial palaces—two shades of green and two of blue, with a fair amount of gold in designs stronger, more graceful, and less crude than anything to be seen in Peking. Dr. Kung suggested that I fly on with him to Sian and join Teilhard and Young down the line at Kaifeng. But weather reports were bad, so we flew back to Peking.

Yesterday was a rather sadly enlightening day. Its main points, a long talk with V.K. Ting, and a specially friendly chat with one of the Survey men. Ting's remarks showed how the wind is blowing for the Cenozoic, but I did not see just what it meant until later in the day.

For three quarters of an hour, Ting talked on geological problems—I realized anew what other Chinese mean about "his ability to talk with authority on things he has not studied sufficiently"! The end of the conversation was the real revelation. Professing to give me "the inside story" (which I already knew!), he said that Wong Wen-hao had "taken him to task for being a needless worrier" when he expressed himself "disturbed about Teilhard and Barbour having gone beyond Chungking."

"Had I been director of the Survey," said Ting, "I would have reprimanded Teilhard severely for disobeying orders. If Teilhard acts like this, what can I say when Dr. Young kicks over the traces, does not do as he is told, and just replies that the foreigners act thus." He added that "the director dismissed the matter as of no significance"!

I was tempted to point out that I understood Wong was too sick to have known anything about this; that Teilhard is not a salaried Survey employee; that the funds were Rockefeller funds to begin with; that Black told me in Washington that he wanted us to get into the Red Basin; that Roger Greene must already have told Ting that Teilhard was to be acting director. Luckily, I had the wit to see that these were *not* Wong's ideas when Black held the Rockefeller purse strings. It was never a case of "taking orders from the directors," because although the Cenozoic is a unit of the Survey, all details were in Black's hands. But he was diplomat enough to get Survey approval of all plans, and while scrupulous never to go counter to Survey ideas, did just what he thought was right. The idea that Teilhard, as acting director, once in the field, could not alter a plan without telegraphing Mr. Hsieh for consent is ridiculous. But it also showed that V.K. had been wrong six weeks ago when he told me that Young was now "fully cooperative." Instead, Young must have been writing back in a critical mood all the time we were up the river. . . .

Previously, Young had handled all cash for the expeditions he made with Teilhard. But this time Olga Hempel, the secretary, had given it directly into Teilhard's hands at Rockefeller direction. This was added to other incidents too trivial to mention, many of them in no way connected with either Teilhard or myself. . . . Young's virulent criticism of Teilhard is disheartening after the way in which Teilhard has helped and trusted him. Anyhow, Wong must have taken Young's story at face value and regarded the four extra days in Szechwan as "disobedience of orders," without noting that it cost the Survey nothing (I had paid for the transportation and the hospitality was a gift from our host). It shows that they want to pull the whole Cenozoic structure back into their own hands and absorb the funds by finding an excuse to discredit Teilhard before the new director is appointed. It also presents a sickening picture of the future prospects for the Cenozoic Laboratory. I did not imagine Ting would sink to this level in assuming that either Teilhard or I would be unreliable. It makes more remarkable what Teilhard has had to work with all these months, and must still wrestle with. . . .

Without Davidson Black to support him, Teilhard's life will be no easy one in the months ahead. In fact, I marvel at his having met some of these smiling faces for so long without disillusion—he has only been in the saddle for three months, and we have been out in the field most of the time. Somehow, it seems harder to get onto a friendly man-to-man relationship in a government organization where everyone is jealous of everyone else, than it was in our surroundings at Yenching where we could only admire the men with whom we worked.

Anyhow, the long and short of it is that I will not delay, once the work is done. I would not be permitted to do any independent work after Black's instructions have been fulfilled, without facing such criticism that obstacles would be placed in my way if I ever came back to China. The latter is still just a possibility—since J.S. Lee's friendliness would welcome any support I could give in his field, even after the Cenozoic Laboratory has closed for good . . .

# 7

# Across the Tsinling Range

BY mid-July we had carried out most of Black's requests. The research of previous seasons had let us reconstruct in broad outline the general stages of landscape evolution in the northern provinces and along the Mongolian border. One or other of us had worked in Chahar, Jehol, Shansi, Shensi, Kansu, Hopei, and Shantung. Suiyuan and the Yellow River Basin had been reconnoitered as far west as Lanchow. The work of the earlier summer months justified us in speaking with some confidence of parts of six more provinces along the axis of the Yangtze Basin as far west as the border of Chinese Tibet. Links with the south coast seemed to tally with what we had noted in the Shanghai-Soochow-Nanking area, with Hangchow and with the studies made by others further down the coast.

One important transition zone had been omitted—that along the Tsinling barrier which separates North and Central China—because for a number of years Honan had been bandit-infested. During the weeks we were on the Yangtze, General Chiang Kai-shek had finally taken the region in hand, and his military outposts were bringing order and stability into the area for the first time in a generation. Teilhard decided to see how far we could go, even though when we set out we were uncertain whether we could work southwest to the headwaters of the Han River. If that failed, we could always turn northwest and come out again at Sian or Tungkwan, on the north flank of the barrier. Discreet diplomatic inquiries secured official approval, and we left Peking again on Tuesday, July 17, and reached Loyang two days later at four in the morning. We expected to need a day to see officials, inquire about routes, and collect a mule caravan. Four days on a bearing south of west would then bring us to the heart of the Eastern Tsinling Range. There we would decide whether to strike south into the Han Basin, or work northwest to Sian.

Reaching Loyang in the dark, we walked 100 yards to the only hotel, where we read and chatted till 8:00, when the baggage car was unlocked and we could wash, shave, and breakfast. We then called on the County Commissioner (*hsien-chang*), a cultured, efficient man of 45 or so, who was cooperative and businesslike. Thanks to him, we did not need to present our credentials to the military command. The *hsien-chang* said that he himself would give us a reliable courier. When we passed out of Loyang jurisdiction, the courier would wire ahead and arrange to introduce us to the next county official. By 10:30, everything was completed, so we slept till lunch.

Eddie Bien had taken Young's place and made an ideal field companion, reasonable, humorous, and understanding of men. He had matured enough to form his own judgments, and stood up against anything Teilhard or I said with which he disagreed. As a result, all went easily. Teilhard's technician-cook was an efficient, cheerful lad—on the job from dawn to dark. In contrast to the provisioning on previous trips, we had brought two fossil boxes filled with food supplies. Eddie, and his wife, Daisy, had shown their usual wisdom in including a set of standard medical supplies which with my own compact kit safeguarded us against all but frostbite, dogs, drowning, and major accidents.

The country thereabouts was said to be quieter than it had been for a dozen years. Licent and others had been waiting since 1920 for a chance to get into Honan, and were reported to be also in the province. We planned to set out the next day, first by bus and thereafter over the mountains on foot with mules. In the afternoon, we discovered that Loyang had only one bus and that it was reported stalled by a wash-out somewhere in the west of the district; so we started by Peking cart instead.

*Changsui,* Honan
Sunday, July 22, 6 P.M.

From Loyang, we had the protection of three armed guards—changed at Loning, the half-way post. The guards are really an excellent crowd. No doubt, they have all been bandits until quite recently! As Eddie Bien points out, it would be hopeless to try to suppress bandits by using soldiers from *outside.* So the authorities pick men familiar with the locality, who are too well known to want to lose their reputations. These men are attached to their own village centers, given just enough authority, pay, and prestige to keep their loyalty, and must carry passports on all their migrations—and it seems to work out remarkably well. Our guards were challenged repeatedly. They produced their papers and we passed at once.

Our troupe eclipses Barnum and Bailey's Circus. Outside one country town, a play was in progress on the stage in front of a temple as we approached. The audience, a hundred strong, deserted *en masse* and tore down the slope, like the herd at Gadara, to watch us pass on the road below—even the players stopped till we had passed! At another point, a pitiful little procession, marching around a temple enclosure with banners and branches, beating gongs and praying for rain, seemed to feel their efforts were not in vain—at least they had our show to talk about for the week—and after all it did rain before nightfall.

Teilhard says he feels quite at home, since the countryside is so like that of Shansi, except for the slightly redder earth. Here there are still cave dwellings in the loess, but he raised the question as to whether this may not be an *older* deposit than the typical northern grey-brown Malan loess, and thus possibly of earlier, Sanmenian, age. The general structures are of basin-and-range type—block-faulted as in Shansi. From Loyang we followed the tips of an *en echelon* line of rifting, with the spurs of the Tsinling offset step by step.

We are quartered in a local village elder's yard, which also serves as a police station. Beyond here, the valley closes in abruptly on both sides —hence the end of the cart road. The three days from Loyang were

103

strenuous—shaken to bits in the Peking cart, alternating with detours on foot. Last night we did not reach Yiying till 10:00 and sat for three quarters of an hour outside the city walls, till the captain of the guard could be called out of bed in the center of the town to examine our credentials. Though such precautions annoy at the time, it shows that they are careful and once we were inside, the city magistrate gave us the best tea we have tasted since leaving Peking, served us supper at 11:30 P.M., and then insisted upon discussing Darwinism. At night, our beds were set up in the court, under the stars: a growing moon lit us till we fell asleep, and sleep came soon after a long day.

Eddie Bien is an *excellent* companion. I could not wish a better any-where—resourceful, keen, and pleasant to work with. As it is virgin territory as far as geological mapping is concerned, all results are to the good . . .

On Tuesday, July 24, we entered the court of the *yamen,* or magistrate's palace, at Lushih on the Loho. From the excitement that greeted our passage through villages along the way, we were evidently the first *yang-kwei-tze* (foreign devils) to enter the valley. The Nanking government had just cleared a nest of bandits and set younger military officers to restore order. These had not fully taken over their new duties, and therefore the pass over the range was not yet thought safe for travellers. For this reason, we had been directed to the military headquarters to be granted access and safe conduct. The new command had just arrived and we, their first official visitors, had appeared before the buildings were swept out. Courtesy required the new district commander to extend us hospitality, and so he kept us waiting in the outer court while he made his office presentable, and pre-pared a meal to welcome us.

Teilhard sat down on the stone steps of the yamen to await developments, and was watching the attempts of three soldiers to unload their gear from the back of a balky mule. One of the men shouted in Chinese that the beast had a nasty temper, but the remark was quite lost on Teilhard, who was still commenting on the truth of a quotation from Li T'ai-po that Young had read

104

from a stone inscription we passed on the Yangtze two months earlier—"It is as hard to travel in Szechwan as to climb to heaven." Just at that moment, one of the men lost his balance, the mule tried to shed his load, and struck out viciously with its hind leg, striking Teilhard on the temple. The blow broke a blood vessel, and within a few seconds he had a blood blister the size of a pigeon's egg over the temporal artery. It took less than five minutes of Bien's diplomacy to commandeer a nearby room in the outer court, unpack, and set up a camp cot. Ice does not exist in a Honan village in July, and the medical orderly of the post had no supplies of any kind except a little ether. Throughout the night, I kept Teilhard's temple cool with constantly changed compresses. I read to him the office of the day from the breviary he had been using in the cart earlier in the afternoon, and waited in fear for the dawn while the candle burned down. Through all of this Teilhard's only concern was for "*ces pauvres gens*" who had prepared a meal with such care, and had no guests to eat it. By morning, the swelling was distinctly reduced, and he wanted to go ahead. But I pointed out that the mule had prevented our writing up the notes on the previous day's traverse. Besides, the Chief of Police had said we might not proceed until a messenger had warned the outposts ahead of our coming.

Within two days, Teilhard was in fit condition to travel. The trail over the range was narrow, so we paid the cart and driver, and put our baggage on mule back. In traditional fashion, the muleteers counterpoised the weight by adding one or two heavy stones to keep the load in balance. Two days later, we threaded the pass over the crest of the range.

On the southern flank, the descent was down a winding gorge, so narrow that the footpath had to cross and recross the stream at every bend. The fourth day began with a three-mile stretch where we had to ford the current knee deep thirteen times. The number must have struck one baggage mule as unlucky, because his ill-balanced load had begun to slip, and, nearing the bank, the beast tried to lie down, after first shedding Teilhard's kit box and bedroll in two feet of water. We bathed, and for an hour sat on the bank with clothing spread on the bushes till the hot sun dried the soaking contents of Teilhard's kit-box, from which he had surreptitiously removed the tin cylinders with his supply of silver dollars.

There was a movie camera in my rucksack, and the last twenty feet of the roll recorded the scene of our total immersion. It was developed after I left, but lay for two years in the Cenozoic file cabinet, and only reached me in America on the eve of the Second World War. So it was fifteen years before Teilhard saw it on a screen at the Museum of Natural History in New York. On viewing the last scene, he jokingly remarked, "Do you not think that if the head of my Order in Rome saw me like that in the middle of the river, he would consider me prematurely unfrocked? Tell me, George, did you ever anywhere find water as cold as that miserable river?"

We continued steadily downstream along the Wulichuan, crested the divide into the Valley of the Lao-kuan-ho, and followed the latter till it became the Tan-kiang, an east bank tributary of the Han River. As usual, Teilhard's eyes and brain were working all the time we were on the move. The Tsinling proved to be not a simple single-fold range, but a more complicated series of thrust folds. The range resulted from the upwarping of a Cenozoic land surface, bevelled across the complex bedrock core of a flexured still older range, long reduced to a low relief surface. Recalling his trips in the northwest, Teilhard noted that the sand and soil deposits containing the *Hipparion* fauna never occur in depressions, but are always found only on high ground, and seem to be restricted to the northern region—Shansi, Shensi, and Kansu. Thus the Tsinling is truly a barrier between North and Central China. In the same way, the chief crops in the north were millet and corn, and we were well down the southern slope before we came to the first sugar cane and rice paddies.

Teilhard found plenty besides the geology to draw his attention, especially when the trail reached lower ground and the broad valley flats. Thus whereas at higher elevations graves were hard to dig on rocky slopes and burial places were marked by limestone tablets, at the lower levels these gave place to mounds of earth from graves dug in the soil of river terraces. Every third man or woman thereabouts seemed to have goitre, suggesting an iodine deficiency in the ground water. Each little village community has its own specialty. One grew the varnish tree used to make lacquer; another cultivated persimmons (*kaki* to Teilhard) from grafts on the sturdy stems of a tree which he instantly rceognized from its bark as the black date or jujube (*Zizyphus*). Quarries near Neichang turned out an excellent lithographic limestone. "Jade" workings at Fushan yielded a greenish variety of diorite, much in demand for the little spheres which Chinese scholars turn over and over in their palms as a psychological vent, much like the Western use of chewing gum. The community at Pantaoching supported itself by making thongs and leather whiplashes. The next village made ink tablets, marbles, and chessmen from fine greywacke or siliceous slate. Northbound coolies packed bulky loads of paper, cloth, dried onions, and umbrellas. When the trail flattened enough for wheeled traffic, the first rickshas we met were piled high with packages of matches, paper, and scrap iron. Chuyangkuan, a famous rebel stronghold in the Ming Dynasty, served as a bandit hold-out till its buildings were burned to the ground in 1932.

Suddenly, we came to a district where foot-binding of all the young girls was still regularly practiced, in contrast to the "independent" counties we had just passed through. Within forty miles of the end of our trek, a ricksha puller who had preceded us had been beaten up, bound, and robbed of his entire load.

107

On the last stretch of the road, they were cultivating tobacco. Here we met the first camel train on its way west, and made the acquaintance of sail-driven wheelbarrows. In fact, for a few coppers, two of us took a wheelbarrow ride for several hundred yards just for the experience. By now, we knew we were in the south. *Kao-liang* (kaffir corn) and maize had given place to rice and tung-oil trees. Water buffalo replaced mules as draft animals.

Finally, on August 12, after twenty-four days on foot, we reached the railway at Hsucheng and caught the northbound express from Hankow, and were in Peking the next day. The day after, Teilhard was back at his desk. Six days later, he saw me off on the train to Manchouli on the Manchurian border, where I caught the Trans-Siberian Express to Moscow and Berlin, and from there to London.

# 8

# The Middle Years

FOR three winters our paths did not cross. Teilhard went back to France twice for prolonged visits between journeys to South China, Java, India, and Burma. I was in England, writing the Yangtze report in the Library of the Royal Geographic Society, lecturing in the University of London, and giving weekly broadcasts on China and North America in the B.B.C.'s educational program for schools. In 1935, I reported on our Yangtze findings to the Geological Society of America, and returned to England on the same boat with Dr. Franz Weidenreich of Frankfurt, who had crossed to New York to be appointed Black's successor by the Rockefeller Foundation. As this was Weidenreich's first chance to speak with anyone who had been directly connected with the Chou-Kou-Tien work, there was plenty to talk about. In 1937, I joined the faculty of the University of Cincinnati and we moved to Ohio.

The following year, Teilhard came to the United States, and we met at scientific gatherings in New York and Washington, and again at the Fourth Pan-Pacific Science Congress in Berkeley, California. In August 1939, Teilhard set out once again for the Orient. A year later he wrote:

Institute of Geo-Biology
Peking, 23 September, 1940

My dear George,
    For weeks, if not months, I have been meaning to write to you. So

109

much has happened since we said goodbye on the platform at Berkeley! I feel the need to regain touch, and to hear again from you soon.

First, as to current affairs.

Since getting back to China a year ago, I have not budged from Peking. I have not stayed so rooted to the spot for years. Several reasons for that. First of all, for the past ten months I have not been in too good shape physically—a vague let-down feeling, depressing one's morale (it is better now). Then, in Weidenreich's absence, the need to keep the laboratory alive. As a result, I had to give up the Yunnan trip this winter —something I truly regretted—possibly my last chance for many a month. By way of compensation, however, I have been at work without let-up, to a degree beyond my hopes. Aside from geological and paleontological studies under way, I have been able to finish up a book on Man—half scientific, half philosophical—into which I have put the gist of the ideas closest to my heart. I hope its publication will not run into trouble from my Order. However, as things stand, I do not see how to get the needed authorizations to print. I am not much worried about finding a publisher. In normal times, I could choose whom I liked.

A further matter. In order to make room for the expansion of the college in Tientsin, we evacuated Licent's Museum, leaving only specimens on exhibit there, and reserve material in storage. All books and equipment were shipped to Peking. For the moment, we are housed— not to say cramped—in a legation-quarter building left empty by the withdrawal of the French soldiers. But almost immediately opposite is a lovely plot of open ground on which we can build—when we have the wherewithal. My idea is to start out again on a new line of study—not of collecting, but of research. At present there are three of us: P. Leroy (zoologist, director), P. Roi (botanist), and myself (provisionally). I think of the organization as an "Institute of Continental Studies" having as its chief objective the story of the evolution of continents—in this case, with Eastern Asia as a model—considered from three angles: sedimentary strata, animal types, and plant life—a sequence of "geo-biological block-diagrams." Since to some ears the term "continental" has a nasty sound, I could not use that word in the title of the institution— which to my way of thinking ought to be "the Institute of Continental Studies." The big problem is to get the right team. I see just what I need. But good men are difficult to secure. Leroy is perfect. Roi fits less well. I'm greatly hoping for Trassaert's return (he is somewhere in France). I also need a good sedimentary petrologist, not to mention a "number one physiographer." For a palaeobotanist I am counting heavily on the collaboration of Fu-jen (University). Archeology seems about to find a home at Yenching (!), where Pei is starting to teach.

No field work whatever for the past three years. We are looking forward to starting again on a modest scale at Chou-Kou-Tien. It is high time we did, if we do not want the Rockefeller Foundation to lose interest. To show that we are still very much alive, we need to publish as much as we can. Due to appear shortly: a memoir by Pei ("Fossils of the Upper Cave"), one of my own ("The Fauna of Locality 18"—most interesting Villefranchian fissure in Mentoukou Valley, where you can see the transition from *Siphneus* with "rooted" teeth to the modern "rootless" type).[20] Finally, sometime in December, a new number of the Bulletin, for which I have written a distinctly ambitious note on "Granitization in China"—something that ought to please Bailey Willis, but will appeal less to certain other people! The argument is supported by copious data and lots of sections. My interpretation may be a bit rash.[21] But there are things I wanted to say clearly once and for all.

Very little news as yet from France, and that only straight from my immediate family. I'm anxious to determine just what forces and what factors still remain for rebuilding things. Britain will probably be our salvation. Henceforth she has the great and finest role to play. From the outset, this war has greatly disgusted and disturbed me, because I felt in a confused way that France had committed herself without conviction and without idealism; just to be free and to "live in peace." And yet, if any truth has come out of the whole business, it is that the pacifists make a serious mistake in defining peace as the *opposite* of war. True peace, the only kind that is biologically desirable and possible, lies in the same direction as war, but *beyond* it: it is the spirit of conquest, transferred to a supra-human objective—to struggle, but all together, and for a goal which unites our energies, instead of dividing them. Would that the present crisis might hasten the birth of this feeling for humanity, for which fundamentally the whole world has a *presentiment* and is searching, but which fails to take shape around an ideal at once definite and tangible. As things stand now, I can naturally not make any plans for the future, but simply work on a day to day basis.

Finally, a query. I just mentioned my friend and colleague, Pierre Leroy, whom you saw here in 1930. At the moment, he is making a complete revision of the Chinese *Lamprotula,* using the altogether unique material collected over a twenty year period, by the Survey, Licent, Bien, and others. (Bien was to do that, but one can no longer count on it.) Leroy, a student of Cuénot, has his French licentiate, but

111

does not have a doctorate. Is there any way for him to get some kind of Ph.D. at an American university on the basis of his *Lamprotula* studies? (I can guarantee the importance of his work, and will take responsibility for the stratigraphic control.) Leroy is a brilliant fellow, and speaks really fluent English. Give me your candid advice, and if the thing is possible administratively, which university do you recommend? Yours? Or California, in view of its circum-Pacific interests? Please give me an answer without delay—possible, or out of the question?

Eddie Bien continues to have disappointments. I've never seen anyone with such a wide circle of friends, and so highly recommended, have such difficulty in securing a scholarship. Camp sent me forms to fill out in April, and they did reach us in Kunming. But since then, not a word! A mail bag must have gone astray. Still another year lost! But I am not giving up yet. I know you are doing your best.

Grabau fares well. He chases his dreams with the old indefatigable zeal. I imagine that some of it will stick, even if only the proof that we need some "new order," and, as it were, a new spirit in Geology. In that sense, Grabau certainly sets us an example and is a *renovateur*.

Sincere and affectionate remembrances to Dorothy.

*De tout coeur,*
Pierre T. C.

P.S. I seem to recall your telling me of having seen fragments of *Lamprotula* in the drill refuse brought up from the well-boring put down at Yenching; but you make no reference to it in the printed report. Am I correct?

For thirty years, my wife and I sent out Christmas cards of our own design, and included, for the benefit of special friends, a mimeographed account of the previous year's doings. During Teilhard's five-year confinement in Peking, his copy had failed to reach him, but on his return to Paris it was again possible to be in touch.

15 rue Monsieur, Paris 7
20 February, '47

My dear George,

It was a great joy to receive the "Barbour Yule-Log for 1946." I had been wondering what had become of you, and still more, of the boys, during these long war years. I see that all prospers and goes ahead hopefully. I am profoundly glad. As far as concerns me, here is a résumé!

Throughout the war, I led a bourgeois existence in Peking, where I landed in August 1939, and where I found myself definitely "trapped" at the moment of Pearl Harbor. In 1940, I established with P. Leroy, P. Licent's successor, the short-lived Institute of Geobiology—a combination of Licent's Museum (with equipment and books shifted to Peking) plus what we could salvage of the Cenozoic Laboratory. A modest, but convenient set-up in a wing of the French barracks, next to the French Legation. There, despite frequent alerts, I managed to work, write, and publish (thanks to Vetch) all interesting material left in my files, my notebooks, and my head. Several of the Institute of Geobiology publications (13 already out) would interest you: "Early Man in China," "The Chinese Neolithic," "Geology of the Western Hills" (in our review, *Geobiologia*), "The Granitization of China." Unfortunately, the entire stock is still at Vetch's, so that I cannot send you any. Distribution is still very incomplete.

Aside from this editorial work, I have been able to do virtually nothing in the field, barring a fairly detailed analysis of the Western Hills, from an angle that seems to me to throw illuminating light on all the continental folding of China. Incidentally, I've been greatly impressed by the extraordinary development of chlorite-bearing rocks (which persist right into the Jurassic, and lead to curious inferences). Apart from that, a single trip into the hills behind Chinwangtao, I was not able to budge from Peking and had to turn my thoughts in on myself. With the result that notable progress was made in my ideas in the philosophico-religious realm—for which, as you know, I have always had a weakness—something of great value to me here, as I shall tell you.

Peace came just when we Frenchmen were beginning to fear that it was going to be *our* turn next to go to concentration camp. Instead, we lived through the great days of the American arrival, bringing back many old friends in uniform. I left Peking a little less than a year ago, without managing to return via America, as I longed to do. And since May 1946, I have settled in Paris, extremely busy, but thus far without any definite position. I am being begged for articles and talks on all sides. I have also lectured at the Sorbonne a number of times. But, actually, I do not hold down any specific appointment. In China, I am still officially "Adviser to the Geological Survey." But if I ever go back there, I expect it would only be for brief visits, and only when the possibility of some definite project develops (such as the reopening of

113

the diggings at Chou-Kou-Tien, or an expedition of some kind). Meanwhile, I am thinking of going to South Africa this coming summer (to try to help work out the age of the Australopithecine fissures). But the matter is still undecided. I have the necessary funds for my own needs, but not for the small team of two or three geologists I would like to have with me. Breuil has been there for a year, following Leakey's Congress in Kenya. If only *you* could come along!

Despite the apparent chaos in the world, I remain optimistic. For, on the whole, events seem to me to be moving in the expected direction; namely, towards a planetary unification of humanity—a supremely risky yet biologically inevitable operation—and one for which we must (and already do) strain all of our best spiritual energies. I should greatly like to be able to talk with you about all that. Sooner or later, I simply must make a trip to America—within two years, I think.

In Peking, at the Survey, only Pei and Huang are left. I think Young is in Nanking. Grabau died two months after I left. I had seen very little of him these years, first because he was confined (in the British Legation, which we could not visit under the Japanese regulations). Also because his last housekeeper (whom he wanted us to call "Mrs. Grabau") was protective and touchy, and kept visitors away. Moreover, from what I heard, his spirits had flagged and he seemed to resent visits. His end came in a dream, in which I hope that some thought of the divine found its way into the rhythms of his pulsations. I would have liked to help him more. I comfort myself with the belief that, in some very special way—a too cramped religion of science—he always devoted himself to a Greater than he. In his own way, he has mounted higher, and that can only bring him nearer to the one common Center of all. Still, there was something sad and incomplete about his going.

And that is the gist of my news. I hope that on your side, one way or another, you can keep at work. I shall be glad to hear of that. And I would be so happy if our paths could meet once again.

Sincere remembrances to that active wife of yours.

Ever affectionately,
Teilhard de Ch.

During the next fortnight, three letters came, the first from Dr. C. van Riet Lowe, Director of the South African Archeological Survey in Johannesburg, asking whether I could possibly join the University of California's South African Expedition. The second was a warm note from Abbé Henri Breuil adding his suasions, and the last was an urgent plea from Dr. Charles Camp, inviting me to join Teilhard, as geomorphologist in the fourth of five parties constituting an expedition, which he was organizing in response to a request from Marshal Jan Smuts, Prime Minister of South Africa. I wrote at once to Teilhard and got an immediate reply.

> 15 rue Monsieur, Paris 7
> 24 March, '47

My dear George,

Your letter of 11 March gave me great pleasure; and further, it greatly excited me, in suggesting that you would consider the possibility of a trip to South Africa. It would be like a dream to find ourselves working there together once again. My own plan is definitely to leave in July—presumably by plane since it seems impossible to get a passage on any boat—and to spend two or three months on the ground, more or less connected with Breuil (who is in Johannesburg already), and with Broom, van Riet, and the Camp-Phillips expedition. With regard to the latter, I a little regret (at long range) that it is spreading itself over too many different objectives; my idea was an effort concentrated on the Australopithecine problem. But the presence of a man of Camp's calibre reassures me. Next to the problem of dating the fissures in the area—which for me is the main question—I would not mind starting my introduction on the spot to the continental story of a block as ancient and stable as Africa. In fact, I have the notion that by contrast it is perhaps just what I need for a somewhat better understanding of Asia. And if we were together, the work would be thrilling. Keep me abreast of your decisions.

Otherwise, nothing new for me here. Did I tell you that since my return it has been the parascientific questions (philosophic and religious) that occupy me most: how to introduce into Christianity, and bring alive thereby, "faith in Man"? Many lectures, and a passionate duel with pessimists, believing and unbelieving (the "existentialists"). I am sending you one of my reprints on this subject.

A thousand good wishes to your active Dorothy.

> And to you, as always, most affectionately,
> Teilhard de Chardin

115

My note of acknowledgment raised questions about the exact date and scope of the projects, to which he replied at once.

15 rue Monsieur, Paris 7
9 April, 1947

My dear George,

Thanks for your letter of 4 April (which came in duplicate). It is not easy for me to answer your questions with precision, for the good reason that I am going "down there" rather in the dark myself. In any case, I wrote Breuil two days ago (by air mail, naturally) to tell him of your possible coming, and asking him to sound out van Riet Lowe, and above all Goodwin (at the Geological Survey at Cape Town). Granted the welcome, and Smuts' attitude in September, it was a matter of my coming with a team of two or three geologists, and the idea was very well received. Naturally, I shall keep you informed.

Once on the ground, my plan is to pay special attention to the region (round Johannesburg and further to the north) where the ancient dolomites are exposed, with their fossiliferous pockets. The same job as at Chou-Kou-Tien, to try to distinguish and date the various fissure deposits: a matter of paleontology, but just as much a physiographic one. It is possible that the work calls for some important moves away from the original base of operations, but thus far I have laid no plans for that. If by remarkable good luck we could arrange to travel together, we ought to stop several days in Kenya to look at the extraordinary Quaternary formations of the region (deposits with fossils and implements, which seem to date from the time when only large lakes formed an almost continuous cover). The British trend-lines take that alignment and the French lines through Madagascar (which I would leave at Nairobi). And so we two old Asiatics will become acquainted with the African continent; and just because we know Asia, perhaps we shall get a clearer view on certain points than the Africans themselves . . . The most disturbing point is that you would be forced to go home so quickly. That does not give us much time . . .

All this still seems to me a dream.

Very affectionately!
Teilhard

By mid-April the University of Cincinnati had granted me leave from administrative duties from June 15 to September

15, thus freeing me to go at the close of the academic year. I was somewhat puzzled by what seemed a lack of agreement among those concerned as to the terminal date, the financing of field expenses, and the possible attitude of some competent scientists as to priorities in certain areas, so I wrote Teilhard on these points, adding that I ought not incur the cost of the round-trip flight without being sure of my ability to contribute in a positive way to the success of the venture within the limits of time at my disposal. His reply was immediate.

15 rue Monsieur, Paris 7
28 April, '47

My dear George,

I received your letter of 24 April this morning. Of course I shall keep it entirely confidential. What you say explains a number of things which it is most useful for me to know, but it does not alter my own plans. As a matter of fact, I am financially quite independent, besides being on the best of terms with all concerned. Van Riet wrote me a charming letter of welcome. I am on excellent terms with Marshal Smuts, and Broom is an old friend. Camp has also written that he will be delighted to regard me as a kind of "collaborator." So I am going out there to see. I think it will be easy for me to avoid embarrassing anyone. In this whole business, it is Camp's feeling that I fail to grasp. I had certainly sensed something at Berkeley in 1939, but I attributed it to the fact that I had stayed with Chaney (at that time, things were not going too well between the two of them). I do not see what clumsiness I might have been guilty of in Peking. (It was I who arranged Camp's visit with the Survey),—unless it was that (with my special knowledge of Chinese) I left to Young the task of piloting Camp over the ground. But that was a pure misunderstanding which, I am convinced, will vanish the first time we meet. On my side, there never was, and never will be, anything but a frank friendship.

As far as you are concerned, Breuil has made it clear to me that you will be welcome (on the side of van Riet and the South Africans). But it would clearly be absurd to risk your good relations with your University on that account. Personally, I have no intention of staying "down there" later than October. Besides I cannot afford it. My whole ambition

117

is to see the problems on the spot, suggest lines of attack on them, or else some principle for their solution. So, do not jeopardize anything to come with me. That would be altogether too much.

Very affectionately,
Teilhard

Three weeks later, he wrote again:

15 rue Monsieur, Paris 7
19 May, '47

My dear George,

Received your letter of 8 May safely. I am delighted that all goes so well, on the side of South Africa! The difficulty still is to secure a flight-passage. It seems that Air-France has decided to open a Paris-Johannesburg flight at the beginning of July. In any case, I have reserved a seat for myself (and one for you) for mid-July. If the line fails to open, I would find some other connection, so that we might travel together, as far as possible. I shall keep you informed.

I know no more than you about the outfit (of the field party). But I think that with a khaki uniform and a spring suit (with an overcoat), one should be able to meet first requirements. Besides, what more can you take by plane? I imagine that one could get other things, if necessary, on the spot. I do not suppose that we shall do much "camping out" in that civilized country.

Most affectionately,
Teilhard

The way ahead now seemed clear. I booked a trans-Atlantic flight to join Teilhard in Paris, and one week after his letter arrived was planning to leave when a cable came telling of his heart attack on June 1. Medical opinion made it quite uncertain whether he would ever be able to go in the field again. A telephone call to California verified the fact that Camp's invitation was for the summer and early autumn of 1947 only, and that if I could not join them, the fourth party would have to be dropped. Since I had cancelled all other plans for the summer, it seemed best to go ahead alone, and to report back to Teilhard whatever

I might learn. At least I could prospect far and wide, and list for him the people and places of importance that he might visit without undue physical effort if he made the recovery for which we all prayed. In that case, he could contemplate a restricted itinerary as soon as he felt able to embark on it.

I reached Johannesburg several weeks before Camp's main expedition docked at Cape Town. This interval gave time for a report on the excavations at Makapan—which I visited at the request of the Bernard Price Foundation for Anthropological Research—and for a valuable circuit to the most important localities in Cape Province. The latter trip was planned by Dr. Alex DuToit, Director Emeritus of the Geological Survey of South Africa and dean of South African geologists, who was my companion for the thousand-mile trek. Prior to his illness, Teilhard had urged that special attention be given to the Transvaal localities. There, my guides were Professor Raymond Dart and Dr. Robert Broom, the discoverers of the Australopithecine man-ape fossils, and Dr. van Riet Lowe, Director of the Archeological Survey, and an authority on Stone Age man in the subcontinent. Observations made that summer were sent back as a long report to Teilhard, and formed the basis of an address to the Ohio Academy of Science the following year.[22] Upon his arrival, Dr. Camp most generously furnished me with the use of a car, which made possible visits to Basutoland, Orange Free State, the eastern margin of Bechuanaland, and outlying parts of the Transvaal, on all of which I reported back to Teilhard and to the Wenner-Gren Foundation, which was already interested in the work in South Africa.

Soon after I returned to Cincinnati, Teilhard wrote from Paris:

15 rue Monsieur, Paris 7
8 October, '47

My dear George,

Your letter of 15 September reached me safely a few days ago, along with your memorandum on the Makapan deposits, which naturally was

119

of intense interest to me. My heart and spirit are still a bit sick at having missed that magnificent trip (with you!) from which I should have learned so much. But I'm happy that you, at least, could profit by the luck that by-passed me. When you have time, I should like to have your ideas about the continental geology of Africa, as compared with that of Asia. For me, that was a second major reason (in addition to the Australopithecines) for wanting to make the trip. And further, when you can, tell me what you think about the relative age and structural relationships between the fissures containing human remains, and those with the Australopithecines. I hope that, somehow or other, you finally received my "Early Man in China" (1941, put out by Vetch at the Grand Hotel in Peking), in which I give the latest interpretation of the succession (from the Miocene fish-beds to the Upper Pleistocene) in the Chou-Kou-Tien caves.

As far as I am concerned, I left the convalescent home at St. Germain early in the month, and came back to rue Monsieur, where, little by little, I am taking up normal life again. I am doing as well as possible, but cannot as yet tell just how much travelling and moving about I will be able to do. In any case, if I have to give up the hunt for fossil man to some extent, it will be to devote myself more and more to the study of what I am calling *The Phenomenon of Man*, i.e., the study of "hominization" in its present phase, something which naturally leads me to search deeper for the relationship and necessary connection between "christianization" and "humanization." I have done much writing and have been speaking a great deal on the subject for the last year, more than ever before, and those questions have had an enthusiastic public reception. Of course, that does not happen without some friction with the authorities in Rome. Fortunately, I am surrounded by a host of faithful and rather influential friends. I think one may say that a break-through has now been achieved in the direction of a "Christian humanism,"[23] definitely oriented with the help of Christ towards the completion of our world of the future. I am sending you, by the same courier (but by surface mail), a separate copy of the *Revue des Questions Scientifiques* on these very issues. I hope they will not strike you as too wild.

No specially interesting news otherwise. Not a word from China for a long time. Saw Dorothy Garrod recently, on her way through Paris. She is well. Have not managed to see Julian Huxley again yet, because of my stay outside Paris, and now he is off once more to Mexico.

I hope that all goes well with your family. Many good wishes to Dorothy.

And to you, "most affectionately, as ever."

Teilhard
Pierre

Next spring (1948), Teilhard was able to cross to New York, where Dr. Paul Fejos offered him the use of a top floor study in the headquarters of the Viking (shortly to become the Wenner-Gren) Foundation on East 71st Street. We met there every time I was in the city.

The Foundation is housed in an architectural masterpiece—a tall, narrow residence in French Renaissance style, with the interior remodelled for office and laboratory use. Teilhard occupied a small room on the fifth floor, reached by an elevator, and lit only by a dormer window and a desk lamp. There was room for a small desk, Teilhard's desk chair, and two seats for visitors separated by a low table, usually with an ash tray and a pile of books. The slope of the roof and the low ceiling made the quarters seem cramped, and one could stand comfortably only in the window embrasure and the inner half of the room. It had no doubt been designed as a servant's bedroom—which Teilhard smilingly agreed was an anachronism that proved the fact of social progress! The hide-out was secluded, yet accessible to his friends, and an extension telephone in the laboratory next door was handy for those who knew the unlisted number, "REpublic 7–2400." An oblique view to the extreme left caught the tree tops in Central Park, and the buildings across the street did not entirely block out the sky. The foundation was centrally situated between Fifth and Madison Avenues, within several blocks of Teilhard's quarters at the St. Ignatius Loyola Residence on Park Avenue, and it was even closer to the apartment of Mrs. Rhoda de Terra, a friend of his India days, where he could rest undisturbed in accordance with his doctor's orders.

One day in April 1948, my wife and I looked in at the Foundation just as Teilhard was in the act of leaving for the offices of the Jesuit weekly, *America,* on East 112th Street. We were bound for Columbia University, so we drove him through Central Park. We had just been at the United Nations, and he was in a mood to talk about the need of working for a better understanding between people of different backgrounds and contrasting ideologies. Some mention was made of Henry Drummond's book *The Ascent of Man,* which Teilhard had seen on my shelves at Yenching in Peking, but had not read. To settle some point under discussion, we went into the library of Union Theological Seminary, and then into an empty classroom where we could talk. There he reiterated his long-held belief in the unity of truth. In the final analysis, he said, science and religion will converge, as knowledge and understanding grow. Evolution must go forward and upward. The present tensions around the world must find a human group solution, if men are to live together in peace. Using his finger as a pointer in the air, he moved it horizontally to show material progress in the world, the aim of the Communists, and then skyward to indicate the upward rise of the spirit in a free Christian and democratic world. The true direction of advance should be the resultant diagonal vector, going *forward and upward* at the same time. This is the direction, he maintained, in which the human race *must* move towards its ultimate goal. The idea had been put forward in his essay, "We Must Save Mankind," first written in 1936, and later printed in *Construire La Terre* (Cahier I, 1958)—but on this occasion we talked about it for two hours.

Some weeks later, on his way back to France, he wrote the following:

*S.S. Nieuw Amsterdam*

My dear George,

At last I am on my way to Paris. Final departure precipitated by the difficulty of securing space on a boat, and also because since May, I have been troubled by a nervous depression that taxed my energy—nor is it for the first time. Forgive me for not writing before I left New York. You and Dorothy were delicious—and inspiring to me in April. Thanks again.

In one way, my lecture plans for next year are in excellent shape (thanks to Fejos). But I learned in New York that I must have an authorization from Rome (from the *General* of my Order). I am confident that I shall get it, especially since making excellent contacts with the authorities at Fordham University during May. But first I must get my nerves in better shape.

All in all, I feel I have gained a lot by this last contact with America. Not much to do with Fossil man, but a great deal on the subject of Living man. You know that the best part of myself is focused on that.

Here on board, I have as fellow traveller a Dutch-American sinologue who knows you (he even met you at Yenching)—Dr. Schumaker —on his way to the Congress in London.

May God assist you and bring you happiness.

Affectionately,<br>Teilhard

I am going back to Paris, 15 rue Monsieur, 7.

At times, Teilhard's modesty went to extremes. One morning early that March, we had been talking for half an hour. Suddenly, he asked whether I could not come back in the late afternoon because he had "to visit a friend." When we met again later in the day, no reference was made to the purpose of that friendly visit. But some days later, I noticed a plasticine bust of Teilhard on a pedestal in the studio of Malvina Hoffman, the sculptor. Four months later, she took the plaster cast across the Atlantic to have it cast in bronze and installed at the Musée d'Art Moderne in Paris. Since it was raining on the dock at Cherbourg, the gang plank was slippery and the porters dropped the bag in which the cast was packed, shattering the plaster. Finding Teilhard in Paris, Malvina persuaded him to give her another sitting. Working under pressure, she modelled a head even more to her satisfaction than the first bust. As Malvina herself put it, "This time even I felt that somehow a bell had been rung and a door closed, with a certain definite thankfulness that I had been able to catch the elusive expression that had evaded me in the earlier attempts." When later I twitted Teilhard on his earlier ultra-secretiveness, he laughed it off, saying that he "did not see why anyone would be in the least interested." He added that whatever sinful pride he might have had in New York ought to have been wiped out "by the inevitable human disintegration" on the dock—"or should one say, by the de-hominization of Teilhard?" I could only protest that the proper term for the earlier "loss of face" should have been "*La De-Pierreization Teilhardienne*"*!*

For several months, no further word reached me. Then he wrote:

Paris 7e, 15 rue Monsieur,
2 October, 1948

My dear George,

I was deeply touched by your letter of September 22. It showed just the best that I expected of your understanding and your friendship. Thank you.

This very night I leave for Rome, where I shall stay until the beginning of November. I received a *most* cordial invitation. Some agreement is to be reached as to the publication of my book, *The Phenomenon of Man,* (written in 1940 . . .). If that goes as I hope, there is a strong chance that I shall receive authorization to present myself to the Collège de France, and eventually give six lectures—in America. In any case, I shall have had my chance to speak from my heart, by telling the supreme authority in a friendly but frank fashion what seems to me the weakness, but also the true strength, of Christianity today. For a neo-humanism pointed towards the Future, we need nothing less than a Christianity, deepened and rethought on the new dimensions of the world around us. Basically—strange to say—Christianity today seems lukewarm and plods along, because Christians have less love and admiration for the Universe than do the pagans. Whereas it is they who ought to be the most truly human among men.

While you were at the London Congress, I was resting quietly in

124

Auvergne, right opposite the chain of volcanoes stretching from Mont Doré to the Puy de Dôme. It was marvellously beautiful. Field-work was out of the question, but fortunately new interests are developing along other lines.

From what I told you above about my Roman plans, it follows that I cannot yet make any precise forecast as to what I shall be doing in 1949. But everything will be settled by the beginning of November. I shall write to you. In any case, I doubt now whether I shall be able to see South Africa, alas!

> Many remembrances to Dorothy,
> Yours very affectionately, as ever,
> Teilhard

As it turned out, neither of his predictions—regarding the immediate outcome at Rome, or the restrictions on his later movements—was to prove correct. But six months elapsed before he wrote again:

> Paris 7, 15 rue Monsieur
> 15 April, '49

My dear George,

Yesterday your letter of 31 March reached me safely—as did the little note sent a fortnight earlier—and touched me deeply. I never felt how truly strong and deep the strength of your friendship has been, and how it has continued to grow from the very first. And that is a source of great joy, a great strength, and a great security.

That said, I think Malvina must have painted too gloomy a picture. It is true that, for a variety of reasons—general policy and failure to understand—my Order paralyzes the expression of ideas that are dear to me. But, as I was convinced at Rome in October, they do it with some hesitation, "to avoid trouble," while showing me much consideration—even affection. So I am not to be pitied as a persecuted man. Further—and this ought to reassure you on my account—the difficulties I face in speaking or expressing my ideas are largely outweighed by the satisfaction I have in seeing my Credo take sharper form in my heart and spirit, and echo more and more "widely" throughout the world—Christian and agnostic alike—around me. The fire is spreading! What more could one ask? I shall send you a little duplicated statement, *"Comment je vois,"* written last summer—perhaps a trifle overcon-

125

densed, but I think you can find your way in it. At bottom, my ideas and basic position remain the same. It is becoming clearer all the time that not only does the Earth turn—but in addition, Humanity is irresistibly caught in a scientifico-social involvement with itself, which nothing can stop. Well, I feel that this movement must (1) be better recognized and defined scientifically; (2) be assessed at its true value, namely, not to make us more mechanical, but to "super-humanize" us; and (3) become more Christian, by showing that it cannot continue to humanize us without being filled with some kind of love directed towards some super-personal Focus or Pole of the whole movement. From this point of view, the Kingdom of God implies, as one of its structural conditions, a certain degree of maturity of the Universe. In other words, Faith in God demands and involves a Faith in Man. Now, I believe that it is for this reconciliation of the two faiths—both in a super-personal transcendence and in a good sought by evolutionary advance—that the spirit of religion is awaiting today. Instead of this, the traditional Church is suspicious of "Faith in Man"; while on the other hand, the Marxists and the humanists (like dear Julian Huxley, cf. *Religion without Revelation*) would bring about an asphyxiation of the world by denying any outcome through convergence in the direction of a Center of super-consciousness! I am convinced that, psychologically, the present crisis will end in an extraordinary renaissance of Christian thought, coinciding on a lower level with the rebirth of the "Human Sense of the Species" (i.e., a sense of the common destiny which is leading Mankind somewhere, through the inevitable phenomenon of Totalization).

Forgive the dissertation. That is the direction of thought in which my life develops increasingly (thanks to the internal logic and to the force of external events). Malvina will have told you that I have just had a bad attack of grippe (simple pleurisy) that for five weeks put me in hospital—where I still am—but it is going much better now. In any case, I shall spend five or six weeks convalescing at St. Germain-en-Laye (address me still at 15 rue Monsieur). Another slice of several months cut out of my life! On this account, the future is "quite a blank for me." And I am not yet in shape to make any plan for America (still less for South Africa). The grippe caught me just after my first lecture at the Sorbonne—it was precisely on the Movement of Humanity "as a whole." I expect I shall spend the summer revising the entire series of five or six lectures.

Will you and Dorothy pray that I remain faithful in the hands, and under the guidance—even the "immobilizing" control—of the Lord? That is the only thing that matters—and something I ask also for you.

More than ever, fraternally yours,
Pierre

In August 1948, I attended the International Geological Congress in London. At the crowded opening session, I was sitting in the gallery of the Royal Albert Hall, when a Danish geologist stopped in the aisle and greeted me by name. As he passed on, a man in the row behind me leaned forward and said, "Pardon me, but I could not help hearing. Are you the Professor Barbour from America to whom I sent a cable the day after Père Teilhard de Chardin suffered a heart attack?" And so I learned from Teilhard's colleague, Père Saint-Seine, the details for which I had waited a year.

Early in August 1949, I was again in England, and crossed the Channel to France to meet our youngest son, Freeland, who was returning from a year's work with the International Refugee Organization in Austria. In Paris, we found Père Saint-Seine in his laboratory and learned that Teilhard was continuing to improve and even talking about going to South Africa. My son and I decided to make the five-hour trip to Clermont-Ferrand.

Athenaeum Club, London
August 28

A memorable weekend. From Clermont-Ferrand the autorail took us in 20 minutes to Lesoux, where Teilhard was on the platform. A few minutes drive brought us to Neuville and on to Les Moulins, where he is spending a month. The estate is one of three belonging to his brother, Joseph, but the latter's lovely daughter is now lady of the manor. She is happily married to a charming and effective viscount, and has three children.

The place is like a *fundus* or Roman villa, where the lord of the demesne is intensely interested in, and well-informed about, the home-farm and vineyards. The view is as wonderful as Teilhard has always claimed. From our bedroom, a window looked southwest to the sweep of skyline from Mont Doré to Mt. du Luguet, with Château Mauzun on a nearer ridge just to the south. A sketch will show you the characteristic landscape—something I have long wanted to see again.

*Château Le Mauzun ,    Auvergne — View from Les Moulins, Neuville, Puy de Dôme. . . .*

Teilhard has much improved, and hopes to go to Africa in 1951. Two unforgettable days, spent sauntering along the avenues, or sitting in the garden, while he spoke of his boyhood with his sister Marguerite, of the threat of hailstorms to the vineyards, and the new value of radio-weather warnings to the *vignerons,* of his slow return to health, and of encouraging contact with mutual friends. Had we any recent word from China? Which of his many friends had I met at the London Congress? On return to Paris would I be sure to look in on the Abbé Breuil, and give him greetings from Les Moulins? And would I be able to go back to Africa within two years? . . .

In his battered attaché case, Freeland carried with him a bronze crucifix. As he unwrapped it, Teilhard sat on the bed listening intently to the story of its recovery. My son and another member of the Salzburg staff of the International Refugee Organization had spent the New Year holiday in Vienna. Wishing a tangible memento of their trip, they entered an antique shop, one of the few doing business on the first of the year. In a dusty cabinet, at the rear of the store, Freeland found an enamelled cross, but on learning the price, he turned away sadly, saying that he did not have half that amount. "Well," said the aged vendor, "in Vienna, we always say it brings luck for the year if the first sale is made at half price. Give me what you have."

When a Russian theological student at the internment camp saw the cross, he at once went down on his knees, and kissed it reverently. "Did you realize," he asked, "that this must be the fourth of the Novgorod crosses, only three of which were known to have survived destruction by Ivan the Terrible in 1570?" When the Orthodox refugees saw it, the exiled Archimandrate offered a large sum of money for it in behalf of his communion. Once Freeland realized its supreme significance to these homeless Christians, he sent it as a gift, and the cross was given the place of honor in the barn which served as their cathedral.

Before Freeland left for Paris, he was invited to a special service of farewell, at which the Archbishop of the Orthodox Church in Exile gave thanks to God for what Freeland's coming among them had meant. Placing a kiss of blessing on his forehead, he put in Freeland's hands the precious cross, as "their gift to the stranger who had come from afar, who understood their needs, who had rekindled their hope, and restored their faith." (On his return to America, Freeland would not take the precious relic to Harvard, lest it come to harm. Instead, he placed it on the study wall at home, where it hangs today above the shelves that hold Teilhard's writings.) The scene was only a few days old, and the memory of it was still vivid, as Freeland spoke of it in that upper room at Les Moulins. Teilhard was deeply touched to hear this first telling of the moving experience, and asked in detail about the life and character of the Orthodox expatriates in this new diaspora. He saw in it a modern parallel to the early isolated Christian communities of which Ferdinand Prat wrote in his *The Theology of St. Paul*—the deep influence of which on Teilhard's thought has been noted by many.

We left Les Moulins late the following day. It was nine months before Teilhard wrote again.

Paris, 9 May 1950

My dear George,

So surprised to get your letter yesterday! From it I judge that Dorothy is all right again. Praise be to God!

Unhappily, I shall not be in Paris the 18th and the 28th. On the 10th I leave for Auvergne, where I expect to stay until September 15th. The annual rest cure. What a pity we shall just miss. Physically, I am in good enough shape to consider the possibility of a trip to South Africa next July (politics and the Viking Fund permitting). Meanwhile, I continue to write essays which Rome prefers not to see me publish—but which are getting around fast *sous le manteau*.[24] I am still thrilled[25] by the question of the human zoological group (its structure, expansion, compression, and convergence). I am thinking of giving some lectures on the subject next year to a group of "advanced students" at the Sorbonne. And naturally, the religious (and mystical) extensions of the problem fascinate me even more. All of us are so in need of a revelation of the face of God on the true scale of the *dimensions* and *organicity* of the Universe as it has recently become apparent all around us.

In the end of September, I shall send you a mimeographed copy of my latest book.

I hope the Barbour tribe prospers, and multiplies.

*En grande affection,* "as ever,"

Pierre
Teilhard

In a sense, this letter, coming after the unforgettable hours at Les Moulins, marked a satisfying close to the ten years spanned by this chapter. Teilhard was once again well enough to contemplate seriously making the South African field trip on which his heart was set—and which was to be realized in 1951.

# 9

# South Africa

TEILHARD'S heart attack in 1947 had thwarted his plan of going to South Africa, and so I left without him on the journey already mentioned in Chapter 8. In view of the improvement in Teilhard's health at Les Moulins, and after receiving the letter which concludes the previous chapter, the following from him came as no surprise five months later:

15 rue Monsieur, Paris 7
11 Nov., '50

My dear George,

I am still altogether "illumined" by our well-nigh "miraculous" meeting at Les Moulins this summer. This meeting, so strange for me right in the Auvergne of my childhood, with a friend so intimately linked with my life in the Far East! Yes, you were indeed kind to come and hunt me out, down there: and I treasure a very sweet memory of it.

This is to tell you, as you can satisfy yourself from the enclosed rough draft of a letter I am sending to Fejos, that my summer plans are taking shape. On several (scientific) grounds I am being encouraged to go out. The doctors raise no objections to the journey. And Breuil writes me that van Riet Lowe will be glad to see me come. I have not yet written to Broom. Naturally, I keep insisting (and it is the truth) that I have no intention of intruding—but only of studying with the South African geologists. Naturally, it would be the realization of a dream to have you down there. Breuil is thinking of returning to Europe for good next March.

A subsidiary reason that drives me to risk the trip is that I feel the moment has come for me to disappear for a time from Paris, where things are getting "too hot" for me personally. For the last six months, the press has been speaking too much about me and my indiscretions. From that point of view, it would be better to give Rome the impression that I am delving back into what people down there call "pure science." There is no need to tell you that my inner position is unchanged—and that the best of my powers are wholly devoted to a smooth transition from the present crisis to "monotheism," i.e., to cooperating in the common task of revealing (or unveiling) a Christian God on the immense scale and organicity of our Universe. To conceive this problem, and to devote myself to it, is the supreme interest that animates and illumines the end of my life.

I hope that all goes well with you, Dorothy, and the boys.

In deep and true affection,
Teilhard

In the same envelope, he enclosed the copy of a letter drafted in English the previous day to the Director of the Viking Fund of the Wenner-Gren Foundation:

15 rue Monsieur, Paris 7
November the 10th, 1950

Dr. Paul Fejos,
The Viking Fund
14, East 71st Str.
New York

My dear Dr. Fejos,

I hope that, a few days ago, Mr. Stresser-Péan (en route for Mexico) brought you, as I asked him, the stencilled copy of the new *Essay on Man*—which, for some reasons of general policy, Rome did not allow me to publish last spring.

This essay I sent you as a most friendly souvenir—and also as an indication that I am still alive, and still more convinced than ever of the utmost importance of a broader scientific approach of Human Phenomenon.

In fact, I feel sufficiently strong for considering once more the possibility of going to South Africa next July, 1951—with G.B. Barbour (of Cincinnati), I hope—for a three or four months trip.

Do you think, quite frankly, that the Viking Fund is not discouraged as far as I am concerned, and would kindly back me once more, in the circumstance?

Just as (and still more urgently than) three years ago, reasons for such a trip are as follows:

"Anthropological importance of *Australopithecidae* is continuously increasing (Breuil, now in S. Africa, wrote me this summer about new and startling finds by Dr. Broom). And yet both the stratigraphical and systematic position of the group is still obscure: due to the fact (I guess) that *something* is overlooked by the South African scientists, either in the geological sequence of the fossiliferous fissures, or in the general physionomy of the fossils. —Now, without overestimating my capacities, I feel that, using my training in Eastern Asia, I might perhaps catch that "something,"—and thus help to advance a question which is presently commanding the whole problem of human phylogeny."

Dr. van Riet Lowe (Archeological Survey of South Africa) is quite willing to introduce me on the sites; and I happen to know personally Dr. Broom.

If I should succeed in this project, my further plan is to go directly from S. Africa to New York, —where I would discuss with you the best way to make use of my observations, and, more generally, to promote a better attack of the problem of "Man as a whole."

Yours, *most* sincerely,
P. Teilhard de Chardin

And I thank you so much for the flow of beautiful publications, — which I am receiving regularly!

In my reply to Teilhard's letter, I explained that I hesitated to ask the Board of Directors of the University of Cincinnati for the second time to extend my customary summer vacation sufficiently to let me visit South Africa and go with him for long enough to secure worthwhile results. I even asked whether he would consider postponing the trip until 1952. My letter enclosed a proof of the outline of Chateau Le Mauzun as sketched from my window at Les Moulins, which was to decorate the card sent out with our annual Yule-log at Christmas time.

133

15 rue Monsieur, Paris 7
14 Dec., '50

My dear George,

Your long letter of November (and the lovely sketch of Mauzun! I am sure my brother would be delighted to have some copies) gave me the greatest pleasure—or rather pure joy.

I fully understand your difficulties about the timing of the dreamt-of trip to Africa. Unhappily, postponing a thing for *one year* at my age ......one hesitates to do so. I shall keep you fully informed as to my plans. In any case, if all works out well, I count on being in Johannesburg by the end of July. If it is still too cold, we shall busy ourselves profitably away from the diggings; studying the collections, and the people.

The thing that worries me at the moment a bit is Fejos' failure thus far to answer my letter. I am *absolutely sure* of his friendship and goodwill. And, provided he has actually received my letter, I am undisturbed: he will do what he can. But what if my letter has miscarried? All the same, I would not dare to write again. He might think I was pushing him, or that I did not have complete trust in his friendship. Do you know of any way to explain what is happening? Maybe he is merely away from the office on tour?

Incidentally, would you believe that this African plan (even if it should never materialize) is helping me immensely? Ever since I informed my Order in Rome diplomatically that I expect to busy myself there with the Australopiths, people seem almost reassured about me; since I have apparently renounced the areas of dangerous thought, to reintegrate research material in the field. Further proof that one should always catch men and things by their foibles.

And in the meantime, I continue to write. I shall probably send you my latest essay at the first opportunity.

Very affectionately,
Teilhard

15 rue Monsieur, Paris 7
16 January, '51

My dear George,

This is to thank you for the Barbour family Yule-log—which interested and pleased me as it does over the years; and to offer you my deepest sympathy (to you and to Dorothy) on the occasion of the

134

death of Dr. Dickinson. A noble figure—and a wonderful ending. Perhaps that is now the thing I most beg of God: to *end well*.

This is also to ask whether you have learned anything about Fejos. I am beginning to be positively worried at receiving no reply from him to my letter of November. (It is twelve days since I sent him a copy of it, together with my best wishes for the New Year: and still no reply). Is he away travelling? or is he sick? I do not have the slightest doubt of his friendship, "but it is just that which puzzles me." Otherwise, I hold to my plan, and I have even reserved a berth on the *Carnarvon Castle* for the 15th of July. If the Viking Fund for some reason cannot support me, I must try to find some other way of getting home. But I need to *know* where I stand. —Can you do anything to help me?

Otherwise, all goes well. I am giving a short series of lectures at the Sorbonne on the phyletic structure of the human group, something which I enjoy.

Again, Happy New Year to all the family,
and as always, very affectionately,
Pierre Teilhard

No doubt this letter will probably cross Fejos' reply. If so, I shall let you know immediately.

The first paragraph of his next letter was one of the few he wrote entirely in English:

15 rue Monsieur, Paris 7
20 Jan., 1951

My dear George,

Naturally, I got Fejos' answer today, just after my letter to you had left. A very good answer, although, of course, Fejos cannot commit himself, waiting for the decision of the board. So, do not bother about anything. Everything is all right, as much as possible.

Nothing new since yesterday. Except that my sister-in-law[26] telephoned me asking for your address; your cards and the sketch of Mauzun had been received safely.

Good luck,
Thanks for everything.
And, most affectionately,
Pierre

15 rue Monsieur, Paris 7
15 May, '51

My dear George,

Thanks for your long letter of 3 May, which only arrived yesterday, due to a delay in the mail.

Here is the situation. So far as concerns myself, I still think of taking the *Carnarvon Castle* at Southampton, on July 12. I hope to be in London between the 6th and the 10th and in Southampton from the 10th on. I plan to take the plane from Cape Town to Johannesburg (or rather the doctor advises it). In Cape Town itself I hope not to have to stay more than a day. So would not the simplest plan probably be to meet at Johannesburg?

Finally, in and around Johannesburg, my one and only interest is in the *pockets* containing Australopithecus (and therefore in the geomorphic history of the region during the Cenozoic). In addition, I should like to take the opportunity of getting some idea of the pre-Cambrian core. But the younger prehistory of the country leaves me cold. So our programs would coincide completely.

As to the question of transportation, it is obviously I who should take care of the expense. I think I have enough money for that.

One more point. On the advice of my doctors, since they dislike the idea of my travelling alone, Rhoda de Terra is managing to escort me —something which I realize represents an appreciable psychological safeguard. A bit humiliating, I recognize, to feel less able to travel alone, as one gets older. . . .

I feel that for you yourself to come, you have to hurdle some difficulties, if you can. "But it is so terribly sweet of you to come." For me, it makes all the difference, both from the point of view of friendship and efficiency, if you can manage to come!

I hope that this new enriching trip, if feasible, will be of great help to you. It seems to me that together we could do the work of four men —particularly since you are already acquainted with the region.

God will decide by the way things develop.

With great affection,
as ever,
Pierre

P.S. The Viking Fund has given me $2,500, and I shall put into the Research Fund what French currency I have. Van Riet has written me a very kind letter of invitation and welcome.

My address in London: 114 Mount Street, London W1 (at the residence of my Order). In Southampton: at the French Consulate (Mr. Blot).

Rhoda de Terra, referred to in the above letter, was Mrs. Helmut de Terra, whom Teilhard had come to know in India. Fortunately, she was glad of an additional reason to follow her professional interests as a writer by adjusting her plans so as to travel to South Africa at the same time. She was thus able to act as Teilhard's courier, taking from his shoulders the business of reservations, baggage shipment, and the other nuisances of travel.

From Paris, they first crossed to London, where we met. Together we visited Dr. Kenneth Oakley in his Curator's Office at the British Museum; talked with Dr. Tindall Hopwood, expert on Kenya primates; and saw Dr. J.T. Robinson, who had just taken over the Transvaal Museum's anthropological laboratory of Dr. Robert Broom, his former chief, who had died since my previous visit to Pretoria.

On July 10, I saw Teilhard off at Waterloo station, to board the Union Castle liner, *S.S. Carnarvon Castle,* which sailed two days later.

While Teilhard was on the ocean, I flew to Nairobi, the plane passing in full sight of Les Moulins, where Freeland and I had visited him two years before. I reached Johannesburg on July 29, in time to meet Teilhard's train from Cape Town three days later. The sea voyage had done him good, and he felt no discomfort from the altitude of the Transvaal, a mile above sea level. But he said he was taking his doctor's orders seriously, at least "for the moment," though he felt so fit that he rebelled at being tethered *"comme un chien."*

A week later, Teilhard was eager to go in the field, and we drove with Dr. van Riet Lowe the twenty miles to Krugersdorp, and on to the Sterkfontein excavation where Teilhard had the satisfaction of turning his pocket-lens on a block of cave-breccia from which Broom had removed the *Plesianthropus* skull.

The first man-ape skull, that of a six-year-old, had been in a travertine deposit at a water-hole on the edge of Bechuanaland.

137

The Kalahari Desert stretches to the north, and the Valley of the Dry Harts, a tributary of the Vaal River, heads back into the limestone of the Cape Plateau. In the millennia since the spring first appeared, herds of zebra, wildebeest, impala, and other ruminants had browsed on the corner of the veldt. From time to time, one of them fell in and drowned or died beside the pool, so that the pockets of travertine filled with what remained of their dismembered skeletons. On learning from Josephine Salmon, one of his students, that baboon skulls had been found in one of these "graveyard pockets," Professor Raymond Dart asked the manager of the Northern Lime Company to urge his quarrymen at Norlim to be on the watch for further fossils, and if any were exposed after blasting, to forward them to the Department of Anatomy in the Medical College of the Witwatersrand University. As a result, in the summer of 1924, a wedding party in progress at the Dart home in Johannesburg was nearly broken up by the unannounced arrival at the kitchen door of the now famous child's skull of the man-ape—the "missing link" Dart named *Australopitheocus africanus*. This seemed to confirm Darwin's belief that the cradle of the human race lay in Africa. The full story is vividly told in Dart's book, *Adventures with the Missing Link*.[27] Teilhard had discussed with Dart the improbability of any close racial relationship between "Dart's Baby" and the stock of *Sinanthropus,* or that of the more primitive hominid which Broom had found in the dripstone filling of the cave at Sterkfontein. Until its exact sub-human status could be decided, it went by Broom's generic name, *Plesianthropus*. From the filling of another cave nearby, Broom also unearthed a vegetarian type, with large grinding molars, hence called *Paranthropus crassidens*. And from a still higher level of the cave filling, Dr. J.T. Robinson, Broom's assistant, had taken parts of the nearly human skull, *Telanthropus*. In 1951, the exact sequence, both in terms of exact age and of anatomical development, was less well understood than it has since become. It was the challenge of this problem that had brought Teilhard to Africa.

138

With a mid-afternoon siesta at an inn on the way home, Teilhard reached the Langham Hotel in Johannesburg, insisting that he felt in better condition and hungrier than when he set out eight hours earlier. He was to go out to dinner with van Riet Lowe, the man to whom we owed the original invitation in 1947. During the intervening four years, van Riet Lowe had carried on excavation in the Makapan Valley, in line with recommendations made in my report to the Bernard Price Foundation after my first visit. Much of the evening, therefore, went to laying plans for the 150-mile trip, to be made as soon as Teilhard felt up to it.

Two days later, we went by rail to Pretoria, and Teilhard spent the next day in J.T. Robinson's laboratory at the Museum, examining the fossils Broom himself had found, especially those of *Paranthropus crassidens,* the giant-toothed man-ape, and Robinson's newer find, the most modern of the series from Swartkrans.

Dr. C.K. Brain, Robinson's research assistant, had just made precise analyses of the proportions of different minerals in samples of sediment taken at two-foot vertical intervals up the fissures at each of the man-ape sites. The variations were charted on graph paper. The resulting curves could mean only changing degrees of aridity in a prevailing dry climate at the time the caves had been open to the air. For the dust wafted into the fissures must have come from the top soil on the ground outside, and this in turn reflected the climatic conditions under which it had formed. Aridity curves for Sterkfontein, Kroomdrai, Swartkrans, and Makapan could be pieced together to give a history of climate variation. When this was done, it proved that the changes in climate tallied closely with the succession of fossil vertebrates excavated from the same horizons. This latter subject being Teilhard's particular interest, there was plenty to talk about that day. Early the next day, August 8, van Riet Lowe joined us and we set out for Makapan.

This locality is full of historic interest. From Pretoria, the "Cape to Cairo" railway strikes north across the bush-veldt, following the old caravan route taken by the Boer *Voortrekkers* in 1835 through a gap in the mountains. The Magalakwin flows north through this pass to join the Limpopo on the northern boundary of the Transvaal, as the pioneer republic was to be called. The river has so low a gradient that, after heavy rain, it backs up, flooding a strip two-thirds of a mile wide for a distance of nearly fifty miles, before entering the narrows. Nylstrom, the settlement on the bank where the pioneers had outspanned for the night—and where we had outspanned for lunch—attests by its name to their error in mistaking this for the headwaters of the Nile, "the River of Egypt," of which the religious-minded settlers had read in their Bibles. At Potgietersrust, five miles beyond the entry to the water gap, a tributary valley heads back into the limestone hills on the east. In 1854, in reprisal for an attack on their outpost settlement there, the Boers drove the native chief Makapan and some two thousand of his tribesmen up the valley side into an immense cave, partially walling up the entrance with stones, and piling it high with brushwood. Setting fire to this, they laid siege to the place for three weeks, and virtually wiped out the tribe. Potgieter and Pretorius, the Boer leaders, were killed. For a century, Makapan's Historic Cave and the village of Potgietersrust have been famous landmarks.

When van Riet Lowe visited the Historic Cave, he found, in a nearby cavern, a block of rubble, evidently an older cave filling, containing layers of broken bones and Old Stone Age tools like those of the Acheul culture of Europe. Traces of ashes led him to call it "the Cave of Hearths." A younger cave slightly higher up the valley yielded artifacts of more advanced type (Pietersburg Neolithic culture recalling the French Solutrean) showing Levallois technique, with which Teilhard was familiar.

The entrance to the Cave of Hearths, where work was in progress when we arrived, is high on the flank of a steep ridge. On an early morning scouting trip in a small Piper Cub plane, I noted an old ridge-track which looked promising. It proved that a jeep could be coaxed to a point above the cave, from which Teilhard could clamber down to the site and then climb on down to the field laboratory in the floor of the valley. He thus saw for himself the exact spot from which the specimens he had handled in the Museum at Johannesburg had come.

The entire trip lasted four days, and Teilhard returned to Johannesburg none the worse. But it was clear that his ability to be in South Africa at all was contingent upon so planning things that expeditions into the field were separated by fallow periods. This accorded with his own preference for a regime that allowed intervals of concentration on whatever manuscript was uppermost on his table. It also meant that there were free periods which I could put to good use in my own studies by visiting districts he would still have found too taxing—though some of these latter were put on his itinerary when he came back in 1953.

In mid-August, I drove down with Professor Basil Cooke, of the University of the Witwatersrand, through Swaziland to Lorenço Marques, the port city of Mozambique, to look for recent changes in the coast line features. On the way back, we spent a night in the Game Reserve of Kruger National Park and explored the headwaters of the Vaal River. We reached Johannesburg in time for me to catch the overnight Kimberly train and thus overtake Teilhard and van Riet Lowe, who had spent the week in the Kimberly area on the Orange Free State border (which I had seen in 1947). At 4.00 A.M., the train stopped, on special request, at Christiana, long enough to discharge its sole detraining passenger on a deserted unlighted platform. With a dismal hoot, it rumbled off into the clear, cold darkness towards Kimberly and left me to take my bearings with a Brunton compass and the stars. I shouldered my baggage and trudged a mile across the veldt in the direction of the Dutch hostelry, which the others were supposed to have reached the previous afternoon. I attempted to enter without arousing anyone, but Teilhard heard the gateman challenging me, and got out of bed to make sure I was installed in the proper room. Pulling his cape over his night clothes, he sat down at once on the bed and proceeded to describe

141

the Vaal River gravels he had seen at Vereeniging on the way down. He had recalled my comments on them of several years before, and was especially pleased at having spotted several more Early Stone Age implements in a gravel layer which had been "picked dry" in 1947, and which had subsequently been further exposed by rain and wind in the interval.

The next morning, we set out by car for the Dry Harts Valley, on the west flank of which a deep Blue Pool is fed by a spring rising from the base of the Transvaal dolomite limestone formation on the edge of the Kaap Plateau. In former days, the lime-charged water came to the surface 300 yards further west, and, as it evaporated in the dry air, precipitated thousands of tons of spring-travertine, or nearly pure lime-sinter—ideal material for the making of quicklime.

In the millennia during which the half-mile platform had been extending itself, enough lime was deposited to keep the Norlim kilns running at full blast for more than two decades. The edge of the travertine platform had been quarried back 1,500 feet to feed them. But enough still remained for Teilhard to reconstruct in imagination the setting in which the troops of baboons and Australopithecus himself must have lived beside the spring on the south edge of the Kalahari Desert.

The next day, Teilhard returned to Johannesburg by car, while I went by rail north along the edge of Bechuanaland to Mafeking, Lobatse, and Gaberones to complete unfinished business relating to the *inselberg* landscape at Kanye, on the eastern margin of the Kalahari Desert. I rejoined Teilhard at the Langham Hotel on September 3, and we spent several days together visiting the Geophysical Laboratory of the Bernard Price Foundation and being entertained by our many hosts at the University of the Witwatersrand. Our last field day was spent revisiting the man-ape sites near Krugersdorp. Here Teilhard examined the exact spot from which Robinson had unearthed the remains of *Telanthropus,* most advanced of the forerunners of *Homo sapiens* to come from the man-ape caves of the district. I did not know that this was to be the last time we would be in the field together.

Late the following afternoon, Basil Cooke, Rhoda de Terra, and Teilhard said *au revoir* as I boarded my plane at Jan Smuts Airport. Five weeks later, Teilhard sailed from Cape Town, as he tells in *Letters from a Traveller*. The night before the *S.S. Boisseven* docked to bring him back across the Atlantic, Teilhard wrote the last geological field letter he ever sent me.

Cape Town, October 20, 1951

My dear George,

I cannot leave dear old Africa—somewhat regretfully—without sending you a few lines telling a little of what has happened here since you left—and saying once again how much I appreciated all you kindly did for me.

Actually, after your departure, I did not make any extended outing—just one brief visit to Pretoria to see Robinson again and look at the full array of his Australopithecus material (thanks to the Nuffield Foundation, he has the means virtually to finish up the Swartkrans dig); and a short walk with Cooke to get a better sight of the Witwatersrand section at Johannesburg. In addition, I had leisurely visits with Dart and Schönland (the latter just as you had said, extremely interesting), —and with Haughton also. It seems to me that I now have an approximate understanding of the situation (geological, paleontological —and psychological).

For a change, I left Johannesburg via Durban. There Chubb, the Museum Curator, took me to see the beatiful section at the mouth of the Umgeni Gorge, to a spot where the ridge (Berea?) commanding Durban is cut from top to bottom for 100 metres by a recently reëxposed quarry face. I would have liked to have you with me, to discuss the mode of formation of the mantle, some 60 feet thick, that overlies the most lovely Dwyka, peppered throughout with boulders. Seen from below, the mantle is of white lime dune sand, so widespread over higher Durban (and on the Bluff), with a blanket of red earth that I could not examine close up. But the most interesting thing was a pocket of huge rounded boulders, up to 30 cm. in diameter, many of them slipped down into the quarry and recurring abundantly at the same elevation on the other side of the Valley, exposed by construction work. These boulders don't appear to be derived from the Dwyka, but seem to represent an old (Pliocene?) river level. At least, that is how I would have explained them at first glance, if you hadn't said that other sections are discrepant.

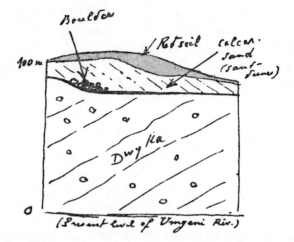

On the way down the coast by boat, I saw a number of interesting things—notably, at East London, the famous crosopterygian fish, *Latimeria*,[28] caught in 1938. But, to my great regret, thanks to bad weather, I failed to get to the Uitenhage passage-beds at Port Elizabeth.[29]

Here (in Cape Town), I have made several interesting excursions with Goodwin—notably to the new site at Elandsfontein (Hopefield culture), 100 miles north of Cape Town. Consolidated dune sand contains an abundant Pleistocene fauna, associated with upper Stellenbosch (or even younger) hand axes—which, as I see it, will call for definite proof that they are in actual *in situ* association with the fauna. I hope I did something useful in directing the good will of those concerned. Cape Town University is shortly to launch a research campaign.

Meanwhile, for a week I have been marking time, waiting for a boat that keeps putting off till tomorrow its date of arrival and departure next day. I am hoping to see Menghin, the prehistorian, at Buenos Aires—and, if all goes well, to reach New York towards the end of November.

I hope all goes well with the grandson. Best regards to you from Rhoda.

Sincere greetings to Dorothy.

Very affectionately yours,
Pierre

For Teilhard, it had evidently been a worthwhile summer; enough to make him anxious to return two years later to visit the places he could not reach in 1951. Though my own research took me back to Africa in 1954 and 1955, we were never in the field together again. For me, it had been a chance to learn how his thinking had developed since he left China.

On one occasion in Johannesburg, he postponed a field trip we were planning because generous hosts had taken tickets for a performance staged at the University. Members of the Sociology and other departments interested in native arts, including dances and music, had arranged an evening program. I always felt that music, other than ecclesiastical music with its natural emotional associations, had little appeal to him. On this occasion, his comments were all on the "primitiveness" of what he saw and heard on stage; his interest centered on what it told him about the social development of *les indigènes,* rather than any pleasure he derived from music as such.

Many hours in Johannesburg went to working on an outline he was preparing for lectures he expected to give on his return to New York.

In a home-letter, I wrote:

Johannesburg, August 21, 1951

P.T. had been working on a lecture he is to give when he gets back to New York, and asked me to help with the English version of the outline he wants for distribution. The subject is "Convergence," as he interprets it. Several reasons make translation peculiarly difficult. He uses new terms to express ideas that have as yet no equivalents—such as complexity-consciousness, or noosphere, analogous to atmosphere, biosphere, lithosphere—coined by his philosopher friend Leroy at the Collège de France. Secondly, there are words to which he seems to attach extensions of meaning not normally covered by the English synonyms. In some of these, I fancy I detect slight changes in connotation from what they seemed to mean on the Yangtze. But that may well be just due to my own lack of comprehension in those days. Part of the trouble is that some words are used in more than one sense, the

145

purely physical, and the other metaphorical or based on analogy. Teilhard's thought slips easily from one sense to the other, without seeming to note the difference as he crosses the boundary. This is true in his "Convergence" paper, when he passes from reflection (as used for light rays or other waves turned back at a boundary surface, or, by extension, for the folding back of strata in overturned anticlines) to reflective contemplation when the memory turns back to past incidents. What a pity we do not differentiate *reflection* of material things, if light is material, from *reflexion* for metaphorical and psychological ideas! When does *conscience* mean consciousness and when does it become conscience?

There are also some English terms that are unfamiliar to him. In physical chemistry, we speak of the "principle of least action," in situations where growing tension of some kind—e.g., increased compression, or progressive cooling—reaches the critical point at which a change of state occurs, so as to minimize the very effect the force was trying to bring about. Thus, at freezing point, further cooling does not at once chill water below 0°C; instead, it converts it to ice (with loss of latent heat), and the temperature falls no further till all the water has become ice. Although Teilhard does use the term *point critique,* the useful term, "principle of least action," must be missing in French.

The main ideas remain as he developed them, as far as the direction of evolution is concerned. He is wrestling with the extension of that axis into the future.

On one occasion when we were discussing ways in which he might have opportunity to speak in public on the fundamental ideas which were later to appear in *The Phenomenon of Man,* I asked whether by the rules of his Order he would be allowed to be a Gifford Lecturer in Scotland.[30] Teilhard had never heard of the series, but pointed out that, in view of the prohibition placed on his discussing his religious views—and even more, of publishing a manuscript—he would be unfaithful to his vows, and be violating part of himself, even to consider it.

Among the last letters which Teilhard wrote me is one which sums up his attitude to death. The fact that it repeats a theme he used in letters to others of his friends only makes it the more telling, coming from a man who himself had faced the loss of so many he loved in his own family.

My son Freeland, whom Teilhard had known as a boy in China, and then met as a young man at Les Moulins in the last week of August 1949, entered Harvard Medical School on his return from service with the International Refugee Organization in Austria. Freeland died during the third year of professional training, presumably of an infection contracted from a patient in the hospital where he was on duty. Five weeks later, Teilhard wrote:

14 East 71st Street, New York
24 February, 1953

My poor, dear friend,

It was only this evening, as the result of a chance phone call to Malvina, that I learned of the blow that has fallen on you and Dorothy. And here was I, thinking that your concern of December was over . . . Dear old friend, how I would that my love and my sympathy might lighten your sorrow, however little.

In such circumstances, I find only one word to say to you—the same one that Termier, the great geologist, used to repeat whenever a great sorrow came into his life—in particular on the death of one of his children—"Whatever happens is to be adored" [*Tout ce qui arrive est adorable*]—at least for him who believes and sees that the entire development of events in the world is permeated and super-animated by the power of love and unity. You and Dorothy are of those who discern, beneath all energy and happening, this wonderful and glowing *Milieu divin.* I am convinced that, for the two of you, and for your other children and grandchildren, what looks like a meaningless catastrophe will transform itself into a kind of blessing. And my wish and hope is that, despite the blow, you will still find (purified, maybe, but still intact) the taste for activity and work—and that, because you will know how to recognize and *adore* a higher form of love, in what has just happened to you.

I hope to see you here in March (for the Wenner-Gren gathering) according to what Malvina tells me. Nothing specially new as to my own doings. I am still working along the same lines—for what I call a "reform" in Anthropology. Two recent books, one by Julian Huxley (*Evolution in Action*) and the other by Charles Galton-Darwin (*The Next Million Years*), make me conscious of the wish and the possibility of writing my own contribution on "the future of the human species" —somewhat in Huxley's sense, but with a much "stronger" emphasis

147

on the biological significance of human convergence (not just a "pool," but a gradual approach to a "Critical Point of Speciation and Reflection"). I shall tell you about that. Meanwhile, I feel a bit exhausted nervously these recent days. That is yet another thing I have got to learn to adore.

May God grant you help, bring you peace, and console you both.
*Je t'embrace.*

Pierre
(Teilhard)

Teilhard returned to South Africa in 1953, but in view of Freeland's death, I did not join him. But in 1954, I was invited back to see the new developments at the Makapan Caves, and to join Wayland in his camp at Nzongesi on the Uganda-Tanganyika border. There, on the Kagera River, he had found Old Stone Age sites. Wayland had also described the Kaiso freshwater lake-beds on which Teilhard wanted further information, since the vertebrate fossils they contained seemed to lie close to the transition between the Tertiary and Quaternary periods. In addition, I had promised Jean Janmart to visit the Pleistocene Angolan diamond fields in Portuguese West Africa.

Several weeks before I left home, Teilhard wrote:

New York, 15 May, '54

My dear George,

Thanks for your letter of the 12th, received yesterday. And my best wishes for a good trip—which I envy—it seems to me that the most important thing you can do (whether with Wayland, or in Angola) is to convince people that the great question in Africa at the moment (as far as paleo-anthropology is concerned) is to throw light on the question of the pre-Chellean (Kafuan) and the Australopithecines. They are far too taken up, it seems to me, with the hand-axe horizon —more dramatic, easier, and more fun. —If you go to Makapan, study carefully the disconformity (or chronologic, lithologic, and climatic "unconformity") between the beds with bi-face tools (above) and the great stalagmite breccias with Australopithecus (below). Kitching is probably hard at work there now. Clark is also on the job at Twin-Rivers. —Robinson has just left with Brain (soil expert) on a long reconnaissance circuit of the breccias in the dolomites (of South West Africa). Maybe you will meet him in Angola!!!

As for myself, I am going modestly to Europe for three months— sailing on the *Flandre* from New York on June 3. So I shall miss you!! In August, I shall no doubt be at Les Moulins. In any case, you can always reach me—until 10 September—at 15 rue Monsieur, Paris 7 (at the review *Études*).

> *Souvenirs respectueux à Dorothy,*
> *Et fidèle affection,*
> Teilhard

I flew back to Cincinnati without stopping in New York. Teaching and college duties crowded out letter writing. To this neglect, I owe the letter Teilhard wrote me from New York on 24 October 1954.

My dear George,

What has become of you? and what kind of general impressions did you bring back from Tanganika (Wayland), Angola (?),[31] and Makapan (van Riet)? Van Riet did write me, but without giving me certain pointers I would have needed to appraise the situation.

As for myself, I spent two months in Paris—useful ones, but all in all rather "hectic" and tiring. On the way back, I saw Oakley in London, but I missed Desmond Clark.

I hope that you will come through New York one of these days— and then we can *talk!*

> My best regards to Dorothy,
> and yours as ever,
> Teilhard

Since the first chance to "come . . . and *talk*" would be when I went to New York to attend meetings in late December, I answered some of his questions in a form that would serve both as a report to the Wenner-Gren Foundation, and as a basis for our next discussion. The last letter he ever sent me is dated December 6, 1954. It shows the same sound, balanced judgment that characterized all his scientific conclusions.

149

*My dear George,*

*Many thanks for your long letter of Nov. 18, which I immediately passed on to Dr. Fejos.*

In the meantime, I received from Robinson and van Riet notice of the discovery of "pebble industry" in gravel overlying the Australopithecus breccias at the Limeworks. I sense that Robinson (very naturally) was inclined to attribute that industry to some Telanthropus. Van Riet is more cautious—and I agree with him. In any case, the find is of first importance. You did well to urge an attack on the beds underlying those in the Cave of Hearths. The work was decided upon in 1953, and entrusted to Kitching. Apparently, something prevented its being undertaken last spring.

Since Desmond Clark seems to have established the fact that the "pebble industry" at Twin Rivers is simply a depauperate Middle Stone Age culture, I am less hopeful about the breccias in Angola. All the same, the baboon skulls (sent by Mouta)[32] which I saw at Arambourg's are so like the fossils from the Makapan Limeworks, that I still hope the Humpata fissures when carefully examined will yield Australopithecus, or a *true* pebble industry.

The Kalambo Site interests me less. What serious work can be done without fossils? . . . At least it will force the African Quaternists to be wary of their "pluvial period" classification. Shall I admit to you that I am still hesitant (not to say skeptical) about the subdivisions of the European Glacial period itself? . . . Under these conditions, Brain's "granulometric" attempt is of the highest interest—provided other lines of attack bear out his conclusions.

Nothing new here. Shall we see you in New York one of these days?

Sincere remembrances to Dorothy,
*and Yours as ever,*
Teilhard

I visited him at the Foundation just before Christmas, and again ten days later. We met once more at the time of the Wenner-Gren annual gathering in early March, within five weeks of his death on Easter Sunday, 1955. Death came in a flash without warning, with friends at his side, in the way for which he had prayed. *"Tout ce qui arrive est adorable."*

150

# EPILOGUE

*Tout ce qui arrive est adorable*

TEILHARD made these words of Termier his own response to hardship or difficulty. This extended even to his attitude in face of criticism. To him what mattered was finding the truth, cost what it might. He was well aware that his ideas were ahead of their time, and, as such, sure to come under fire, alike in the material, and in the philosophic and religious fields. But he counted on a frank facing of the issues by men of good-will, convinced that Truth must ultimately conquer. For fundamentally, Truth must be a unity, not an entity in which facts in one sphere remain permanently contradictory to other types of reality.

In 1936, he sent me as a cloth-bound booklet, *How I Believe* —his own translation of the French original of his credo, *Comment je crois,* which he had set down prior to our Yangtze expedition of 1934. It is inscribed "*A mon ami G.B. (un autre côté de moi-meme) Teilhard.*" Facing the title-page are printed the four pillars of his faith:

I believe the Universe is an Evolution.

I believe that the Evolution goes towards Spirit.

I believe that the Spirit achieves itself in the Personal.

I believe that the Personal Supreme is the Universal Christ.

At the outset, Teilhard recognized that two sides of life often seem essentially opposed—by temperament and profession he is "a Child of the Earth," while by intellect and training he belongs among "the Children of Heaven." And yet in depth he was

151

conscious of no discordance, and for him the two sides merged without conflict.

On the purely scientific side, criticism came mainly from those biologists whose training led them to different interpretations of the evolutionary process. G.G. Simpson in America and P.B. Medawar in England are cases in point. Yet at the same time Dobzhansky (U.S.), Huxley and Raven (England), Piveteau (France), and Waddington (Scotland) recognized that, even though experiment can not "prove" the correctness of Teilhard's conclusions, the latter are not contrary to scientifically established facts. Some geologists feel that Teilhard ventured into their specialized fields without full enough study of what was written in recent years—a thing Teilhard himself was ready to admit with regret. But in his own field of paleontology, his observations are unchallenged. True, where the forebears of man are concerned, there is still debate among authorities as to the exact relationships between different sub-human species, but the general truth of Teilhard's position is shared by anthropologists of the highest standing.

The severest attack came from theologians and philosophers. In the field of health, disease is the failure of some organ or function to act as it naturally should. The doctor's task is to bring about a return to the conditions under which nature may re-assert itself. For Teilhard, evil, like pain, certainly exists in life, but is basically a lapse in goodness, rather than a positive malignancy. Hatred is overcome only by the positive action of love, the one great unifying force in the world. It was Teilhard's lack of emphasis on sin that first brought him under the criticism of his superiors. To them, he seemed to be belittling the importance of the devil, the fall of mankind, penitence and redemption, in the form insisted upon by the Church. Teilhard found warrant for his attitude in the recorded sayings of St. Paul, St. Augustine, and other of the Fathers. His own answer to those critics who blamed him for giving so little attention to evil and sin is printed in the final pages of the *Phenomenon* as "Some Remarks on the Place and Part of Evil in a World in Evolution"—originally a three-page addition, written in Rome on 28 October, 1948, at the end of his defense of his position before the General of his Order.

Teilhard had expected that the wisdom of the Church would seek a frank and honest reappraisal of his reading of history and experience, and he believed that in so doing his judges would come to share his conviction that reality cannot be in conflict with itself in religion, science, or life. If this were re-thought, with the objectivity that Paul seemed to approve, and in light of the new data of science, the God-planned oneness in the universe would be manifest. It therefore came as a profound shock to find that, despite the friendly welcome he met upon arrival in Rome, such a reappraisal was denied. Most of his critics, bound by the modes of thought and definitions of past centuries, and by their training, temperament, and emotion, could consider truth only in one realm at a time. They were not prepared to face the risk of trying to see the greater unity of truth which Teilhard had glimpsed. He readily admitted that some of what he believed could not today be established by foot-rule or microscope. For a long time to come, there would be gaps in our system of knowledge even about the material world, and the answers would have to be taken on faith until more is understood. But in *The Phenomenon of Man*, he professed only to point out the direction in which the future would find answers to unsolved questions.

Part of Teilhard's difficulty in transmitting his ideas lay in his figurative use of words which commonly carry a somewhat different spatial meaning (such as "within," "without," "radial," "tangential"), part in his adoption of new terms—some coined by others, some of his own making—for concepts not previously formulated. He explains most of these when they first appear in his writings, and even at times made lists of them, but left us no fool-proof set of definitions. Even Claude Cuènot, his biographer, recognizes that the Teilhard lexicon which he prepared leaves much to be desired. For those who know Teilhard's writings only in translation, there is the added problem of following his ideas through an interpreter.

One startling example of this language difficulty is evident in the Herbert Spenser Lecture for 1963, in which Professor P.B. Medawar, the distinguished Nobel Prize winner, puts forward with obvious pride his unorthodox concept that evolution must be threefold—chemical, organic, and "psychosocial." This comes strangely from a man who four years earlier was ready to stigmatize Teilhard as a "self-deceiving" naturalist who "achieved a moderate proficiency in an unexacting kind of science." Had the Cambridge Professor's about-face been a back-handed apology for his earlier unseemly contempt, he would surely, as a scientist, have been ready to credit Teilhard. Otherwise, we may blame Dr. Medawar's regrettable ignorance of French, or his pontifical disinclination to make the effort needed to understand the book he was asked to review. Unfortunately for Alfred Nobel and for biology, Teilhard's name will be remembered, even if constantly mispronounced, centuries after Dr. Medawar's lapse has been long forgotten.

In the last lecture of his Background Series delivered in 1960 at University College in Jamaica, Conrad H. Washington, Professor of Animal Genetics in the University of Edinburgh, recognizes what he terms "sociogenetic transmission" as the new mechanism by which man, through the development of language, "alters his relations with the rest of the world as the generations pass." After a masterly survey of the upward evolution of life through its early stages, he refers to evolutionary progress as "something which should guide man's ethical strivings," and cites with approval Sir Julian Huxley's ethical humanism, before going on to discussing the vital importance of "self-awareness." "Are we not forced to conclude that even in the simplest inanimate things there is something which belongs to the same realm of being as 'self-awareness'? It need not, of course, resemble our self-awareness any more closely, say, than the passage of an electric current down a wire resembles the operation of a complex calculating machine, or the operation of the nerve cells in our brains. Such ideas have been expressed . . . by Teilhard de Chardin who maintains that, as well as what he calls the 'without' of things, which we can observe, there is always a 'within' which we cannot observe except in ourselves, but which has the quality of self-awareness. I cannot myself follow all the conclusions that Teilhard draws from this, but the basic idea finds support from many quarters. . . . We confront in the phenomenon of self-awareness a basic mystery of the free will which is inextricably involved in self-awareness; our whole understanding of the external world is deduced from what we consciously perceive."

The list of outstanding scientists and thinkers who were ready to sponsor the original publication of *Le phénomène humain* was omitted from the English version. In itself it is a striking testimony to the high opinion in which Teilhard's ideas were already held in 1955. Today the list would have been much longer. It is only as men come to recognize Pierre Teilhard as a scientist and thinker in his own right, that his full stature and importance will be realized. Actually, the non-French-speaking world still awaits a restatement of Teilhard's ideas in simple words that meet the needs of humanity today. His great contribution lay in discerning an underlying axis, or direction, of evolutionary progress, in a world where man is the most advanced animate creature. Comparable interpretations in the biological world were reached independently by Bernard Rensch and Julian Huxley. Hitherto, ignorance of an ultimate goal towards which life is moving forward has prevented us from distinguishing those features that mark an upward advance, from those which characterize lines of recession or failure. Now, by consciously directing thought and action, men have freedom to ally themselves with the small but growing group which holds the hope of the

155

future, rather than joining the larger unthinking body of mankind that is dooming itself to stand still or fall away, as the steady upward advance continues. The sphere in which future progress must take place is in the field of personality, where the human spirit operates on a higher plane than anything known in the instincts or consciousness of the lower animals, or indeed in man himself until he attained his present potential understanding and self-awareness. Since man is free to choose consciously, he will continue to make mistakes. But man can learn from experience, and in so doing molds his character, and thus augments the total force converging towards a higher level of existence. Through a clearer perception of the external world, and a deeper understanding of his inner being, he may comprehend better the world into which he was born, and the work of the God who designed it. Teilhard sees in Christ the highest expression of personality—the goal towards which creation is moving, and the ultimate objective of the human race, for, as Teilhard himself puts it, "*Tout ce qui monte converge.*"

It would be hard to better the conclusion of Dobzhansky's free rendering of a passage which ends the last chapter of his book, *Mankind Evolving:* "To modern man, so forlorn and spiritually embattled in this vast and ostensibly meaningless universe, Teilhard de Chardin's evolutionary idea comes as a ray of hope. It fits the requirements of our time.

"For 'Man is not the center of the universe as was naively believed in the past, but something much more beautiful—Man, the ascending arrow of the great biological synthesis. Man is the last-born, the keenest, the most complex, the most subtle of the successive layers of life. This is nothing less than a fundamental vision. And I shall leave it at that.'"

# NOTES

1. *Pierre Teilhard de Chardin. Les grandes étapes de son evolution,* Librarie Plon, Paris 1958. English translation: *Teilhard de Chardin. A Biographical Study,* Helicon, Baltimore 1965.

2. Editions du Seuil, Paris 1962. English translation now being prepared by Signet Books, New York.

3. Harper and Row, New York 1962.

4. Harper and Row, New York 1962.

5. Robert Francoeur, editor, Helicon Press, Baltimore 1961.

6. The French originals may be consulted at the Foundation Teilhard de Chardin in Paris.

7. English translation, Harper and Row, New York 1959.

8. Under later Communist rule, the more honorable earlier name has been restored.

9. This must have formed as dripstone from the roof of a cavern, later completely choked with broken rock from the ceiling, interlayered with water-borne sand washed into the huge cavity.

10. Freshwater bivalves found near the coast.

11. There is no exact English equivalent for the useful French terms *emboité* and *déboité* as applied to contracting and expanding zones of freshwater sediment. "Off-lap" and "overlap" usually apply to marine strata.

12. "Mutually incompatible."

13. Presumably H. S. Wang, who went with us to C.K.T. in October 1929.

14. Teilhard knew that I had spent a winter in California on leaving China. But he was apparently unaware of the fact that the scenic "fossil shore-lines" of the Pacific, from Mexico to beyond the Canadian border, had been under study by competent men for more than a quarter of a century. Answers to his questions were already in print, some in the Congress handbooks. The lacuna (. . .) covers questions

157

he asked only because he hoped to find American parallels to Pleistocene features on the other side of the Pacific, where conditions had been very different.

15. Teilhard's misnomer for the street on which Grabau lived near the Survey, in the West City of Peking. Grabau's daughter, Josephine, was living in New Jersey.

16. Our findings were reported in three publications:

G. Barbour, *Physiographic History of the Yangtze Valley*, Geological Survey of China, Memoir Series A no. 14, 1935.

P. Teilhard and C. C. Young, *Cenozoic Sequence in the Yangtze Valley*, Geological Society of China, Bulletin 14, 1935, pages 179–210.

P. Teilhard and C. C. Young, *Mongolian Amblypod in the Red Beds of Ichang*, Geological Society of China, Bulletin 15, 1936, pages 217–223.

17. *Teilhard de Chardin, Les grandes étapes de son evolution*, page 224.

18. J. Leighton Stuart, President of Yenching University, later U.S. ambassador to China.

19. Minister of Finance, brother-in-law of Sun Yat-sen and Chiang Kai-shek, 75th direct lineal descendant of Confucius.

20. During the slow process of evolution, slight changes take place in the organs and bony-skeleton of animals, as the generations pass. In the case of a creature that is extinct, the fossil teeth, feet, and braincase are specially useful as clues to its feeding habits, posture or locomotion, and its ability. Teilhard noted that the prehistoric hamsters had teeth firmly rooted in their jaws, whereas their living descendants continue to thrive with only "milk-teeth."

21. A world-wide dispute was going on at the time as to whether igneous rocks such as granite and basalt formed only as the result of crystallizing from original melts, following the classical tradition, or whether they might not also result from the fusing, in whole or in part, of older rocks of all kinds, including sandstones, shales, and limestones, as the consequence of radioactive heating, severe pressure or chemical reaction underground. Teilhard had evidence supporting the second view.

22. G. Barbour, *Ape or Man? An Incomplete Chapter of Human History from South Africa*, Presidential Address, Ohio Academy of Science, Ohio Journal of Science, vol. 49, 1949, pages 129–145.

23. Teilhard's use of the terms "Christian humanism" and "neo-humanism" appear to involve a contradiction, since the word "humanism"

158

as usually defined means a religion focused upon a belief of man, and definitely excludes any belief in God or divine action.

24. *Mais qui courent beaucoup sous le manteau.*

25. *Passioné.*

26. Mme. Joseph Teilhard.

27. Harper and Row, New York 1959.

28. At intervals since 1938, fishermen off the coast of Madagascar have caught at 100 fathoms fish weighing over 100 pounds, that are classic examples of the ability of living things to transmit to their descendants a pattern of growth which may persist without change through millions of generations. *Latimeria* today shows features of skeleton, lungs, and other organs, first found in fish of the Devonian Period, 300,000,000 years ago. Apparently, conditions on the sea-floor at that depth have remained so stable, and the creature was so perfectly adjusted to its environment, that no further evolution was necessary for it to persist unaltered. The cumbersome fish never survives capture, because blood and tissue that thrive under pressure of 50 pounds per square inch, release dissolved gases and "boil" on suddenly reaching the surface, unless slowly decompressed like a deep-water diver with the "bends". The carcasses captured are invariably ruptured and have to be reconstructed for exhibit, the blue-green iridescence turning to dull brown a few hours after death. The East London specimen which Teilhard saw was stuffed, painted, and mounted some days after it had been caught. It had been a "living fossil."

On June 6, 1961, I was in the Department of Comparative Anatomy on the rue Buffon in Paris, when Dr. E. O. Stensio of Stockholm saw for the first time the specimen flown refrigerated within a few hours after it was hauled up, and superbly mounted by Dr. Millot. Stensio noted a dozen features he had pictured from his Devonian prototype, several without knowing what purpose they served in the living animal.

29. Uitenhage is one of the few places where layers of sand containing Cretaceous fossils are underlain by still more ancient seafloor deposits, which must, therefore, date from the immediately preceding Jurassic period. Such "passage beds" are apt to yield a fauna of transitional character, thus showing evolution "caught in the act."

30. In establishing the terms of his legacy in 1885, Lord Gifford wrote:

> I wish the lecturers to treat their subject as a strictly natural
> science, the greatest of all possible sciences, indeed in one

sense the only science, that of Infinite Being, without reference to or reliance on any supposed special or exceptional or
so-called miraculous revelation. I wish it to be considered just
as astronomy or chemistry is. I have intentionally indicated,
in describing the subject of the lectures, the general aspect
which I wish the lectures to bear, but the lecturers shall be
under no restraint whatever in their treatment of their
theme . . .

31. Teilhard had evidently forgotten Jean Janmart's name.

32. Dr. F. Mouta, Portuguese Government geologist in Mozambique,
had sent to Paris, for identification, primate fossils found by Dr. L.S.B.
Leakey and others at sites I had visited in Angola with Dr. Janmart
during the summer. My letter had drawn Teilhard's attention to their
value in trying to date the cultural horizons.